THE HEALTHCARE EXECUTIVE'S GUIDE TO ALLOCATING CAPITAL

THE HEALTHCARE EXECUTIVE'S GUIDE TO ALLOCATING CAPITAL

Jason H. Sussman

ACHE Management Series

Your board, staff, or clients may also benefit from this book's insight. For more information on quantity discounts, contact the Health Administration Press marketing manager at 312/424-9470.

11   10   09   08   07   5   4   3   2   1

Library of Congress Cataloging-in-Publication Data

Sussman, Jason H.
    The healthcare executive's guide to allocating capital / Jason H. Sussman.
        p. cm.
    Includes bibliographical references.
    ISBN-13: 978-1-56793-956-9
    ISBN-10: 1-56793-956-2
    1. Medical care—Finance. 2. Capital. I. Title

RA410.5.S87 2007
388.4'33621—dc22   2007061352

The paper used in this publication meets the minimum requirements of American National Standards for Information Sciences—Permanence of Paper for Printed Library Materials, ANSI z39.48–1984.∞ ™

Health Administration Press   Acquisitions manager: Audrey Kaufman
A division of the Foundation of   Project manager: Amanda Bove
    the American College of   Layout editor: Chris Underdown
    Healthcare Executives
One North Franklin Street, Suite 1700
Chicago, IL 60606-3424
(312) 424-2800

Contents

Preface

AFTER WORKING WITH healthcare organizations of all types for more than 25 years, I am still surprised by how unique each organization is in its own right. Also clear to me now is the fact that no matter how large, complex, or mission driven the hospital or health system, its ultimate success is a direct function of its ability to manage effectively within a consistent and transparent structure.

This reflects a healthcare environment that has changed considerably since the late 1970s. At that time, healthcare organizations in large part were run by leaders who moved their organizations without using a team-based structure. Interestingly, during that and subsequent decades, there was a high degree of dissatisfaction with the overall strategic decision-making processes in such healthcare organizations. The processes were too political, too disjointed, and too qualitative.

In the 1980s and into the 1990s, observation of and interaction with the executives of many healthcare organizations taught me volumes about their capital-investment decision making and decision making in general. At the same time, an extended dialog between Kaufman, Hall & Associates and General Electric (GE) Medical Systems provided a direct window on "the GE approach" to financial planning and capital allocation and management. The GE process was structured, heavily analytical, and transparent. Why were the processes used by the healthcare organizations I observed and those used by GE so starkly different?

The answer is, "They shouldn't have been and shouldn't continue to be into the future." Beginning in the 1980s, changes in payment structures that removed the economic safety net offered by Medicare reimbursement in its early years, the advent of significant nonhospital competition, and increasing operating complexity transformed healthcare's environment to one that needed to be much more corporate in nature. The new environment requires not-for-profit healthcare organizations to apply the corporate finance–based decision-making approach used by *Fortune* 100 companies.

During the past 10 to 15 years, my partner, Kenneth Kaufman, and I have refined corporate capital management concepts and logistics to fit the unique operating and cultural aspects of today's healthcare organizations. We have been working closely with all types of hospitals and health systems to improve the quality of their capital decision-making processes through application of a best-practice corporate finance approach.

This book describes the best-practice concepts, structures, and approaches that have been identified, developed, and successfully implemented in healthcare organizations during the past decade. It is intended to provide a single reference source for healthcare executives and managers looking to design a new capital management process or to redesign an existing process. Real examples of successful approaches (and unsuccessful approaches, as helpful) are included to guide the reader on the practical application of best-practice principles. The case study included in Chapter Nine illustrates the effort and patience required to design and implement a truly corporate finance–based capital management process. Although the organization's name has been changed for confidentiality purposes, I hope that the insights provided by the organization's vice president of finance prove helpful to others as they endeavor to make the transition to a new capital management process.

Implementing a corporate finance–based capital management process involves major organizational change—change in structure, change in communication, and often change in the definition of what is important to the organization's growth and vitality. The underlying structure of any organization's decision-making process should be addressed with care. The right structure and process must be created and its support ensured throughout the organization, commencing at the top.

This book has been a work in process for many years. It has benefited from the work of colleagues at Kaufman Hall and from the imagination and focus of client healthcare organizations. New ideas, practical applications, and evolving best practices come from a wide range of sources. I have worked hard to include the "best of the best" from clients and colleagues, and I thank them all for their input to this book.

I cannot begin to thank Nancy Gorham Haiman enough for the intelligent and professional oversight she provided as consultant and editor for this book. She helped to bring a wealth of experiences and concepts together within one book, which will serve as a widely usable reference for healthcare executives and managers industrywide. I leave it to the book itself to give readers a sense of Nancy's skill and vision.

Finally, I want to thank my wife, Karen, who gives me constant support and encouragement. She endures all of the nights when I am on the road working with clients and those at home spent working on this book and other projects. Karen provides me with the foundation on which I continue to build my career. It is hard to imagine how my life would be complete without her.

Introduction

Publication Goals

In an environment of scarce resources, increasing competition, and significant requirements for capital investment, healthcare executives nationwide must allocate available capital to those initiatives that will best meet the strategic objectives of their organizations while enhancing financial performance.

Few healthcare organizations have sufficient capital capacity to meet their comprehensive, strategic capital requirements. Their leaders must make choices. How much capital to spend and what projects on which to spend dollars are critical decisions with long-term strategic and financial implications. Executives frequently struggle with how to make these decisions. Wide variations exist in the decision-making processes used to allocate scarce capital resources in U.S. healthcare organizations.

Many organizations implement portions of a best-practice capital allocation and management process and are very adept at managing those aspects. Few organizations address capital allocation and management on a comprehensive basis. This reflects the cultural and organizational challenges associated with establishing and revising a strategic decision-making process. Healthcare executives often dislike the process used to allocate capital in their organizations, but they are hard-pressed to identify and implement the needed framework of organizational and practical changes to achieve improvements.

Decision-making authority is often a key issue. At what level should capital decisions be made, and who should be involved in review and approval? Issues surrounding appropriate decision criteria are also critical. Are criteria defined and consistently applied organization-wide? Technical challenges — such as how to calculate capital availability, the qualitative and quantitative metrics required for project analysis and review, and the mechanics of integrating the capital allocation and management process with the organization's strategic and financial planning — are numerous and can also present significant roadblocks.

An organization's ability to address these issues largely determines its strategic future. The capital markets, including the rating agencies, bond insurers, and institutional investors that review an organization's credit-worthiness, view capital management as an integral component of an organization's comprehensive decision-making process. It establishes (or not) the organization's management credibility and ability to sustain successful performance.

The *Healthcare Executive's Guide to Allocating Capital* provides a framework and a step-by-step approach to disciplined capital management decision making and process implementation. Applicable to all healthcare organizations — from small community hospitals to large healthcare systems — the approach provides the needed financial context for an organization to achieve and sustain competitive, strategic financial performance.

Contents Overview

The *Healthcare Executive's Guide to Allocating Capital* includes nine chapters that describe a best-practice capital management framework and process. Each chapter covers a distinct topic. Examples of framework and process application in different settings — such as a community hospital and a small, multihospital health system — are provided, as appropriate.

Chapter One, "Capital Allocation and Management Essentials," defines capital allocation and management and describes how it is integrally linked through the capital management cycle with the organization's strategic, financial, and capital planning and budgeting processes. It describes the significance of high-quality capital management, common approaches to allocating capital in healthcare organizations today, and the characteristics of a best-practice process. The chapter concludes with a contemporary definition of capital and the types of investments covered through a corporate financed–based approach.

Chapter Two, "Constructing a Best-Practice Capital Management Framework," provides guidance on how to construct a framework that will support best-practice capital management. The framework has concrete objectives—consistency, standardization, transparency, known timing, and use of analytics—and core principles, such as equal access to dollars, one-batch review, and portfolio decision making. The chapter also describes how organizations can design or redesign their existing processes and establish a successful governance structure and process calendar that will drive organization-wide, integrated planning and decision making.

Chapter Three, "Determining the Capital Constraint," describes the process executives can use to determine how much the organization can afford to spend in the near term and long term. The chapter provides details on the mechanics involved in calculating the capital constraint (net cash available for capital spending), which include determining cash flow, debt proceeds, philanthropic funds, working capital, principal payments, carry-forward capital, cash reserve requirements, and other sources and uses of cash. The chapter includes an example of a five-year capital constraint calculation at a two-hospital system and concludes with a description of the need to defend the capital constraint from common challenges, such as those posed by operating leases and information technology.

Chapter Four, "Defining the Capital Pools," describes how executives should determine the pools into which the total capital dollars available for spending will be divided and managed. A recommended approach using three pools—(1) threshold capital, defined as the pool for any capital expenditure above a certain dollar amount that will require comprehensive analysis and centralized review; (2) nonthreshold capital, defined as the pool for requests with associated costs below the threshold dollar amount; and (3) contingency, defined as the pool that supports and provides reserves for projects occurring through the other two pools—is outlined, as are methods for funding and managing the pools.

Chapter Five, "Allocating and Evaluating Nonthreshold Capital," provides a recommended approach to allocating capital on a decentralized basis for requests with costs below the threshold dollar amount. The chapter describes how to handle allocation to revenue-generating units as well as to nonprofitable, nonrevenue-producing, and small operating units. It also provides information on evaluating nonthreshold capital projects using standardized capital-request forms, which enhance an organization's ability to review the appropriateness of estimated costs and timing and to explore opportunities to combine requests to gain purchasing power and efficiency. A sample form is provided.

Chapter Six, "Evaluating Threshold Capital Investment Opportunities," describes the recommended one-batch process for reviewing requests for and allocating capital to large-dollar, threshold capital initiatives. The chapter outlines the key elements of business plans or standardized project review forms used with each request and offers example provisions for addressing emergency and off-cycle requests. Corporate finance–based techniques for quantitative return on investment analysis are described in detail, including net present value analysis and expected net present value analysis. The chapter describes how to quantify qualitative measures and appropriately weight both quantitative and qualitative criteria.

Chapter Seven, "Using a Portfolio Approach to Threshold Project Selection," describes how organizations combine the information obtained through quantitative and qualitative analyses to select a portfolio of threshold projects that balances margin and mission. The chapter outlines the process involved in constructing both quantitatively based and qualitatively based rankings of projects and in uniting these rankings to select a portfolio of initiatives that will ensure the organization's continued competitive performance.

Chapter Eight, "The Post-Allocation Process," describes what should occur after allocation decisions are made. Activities covered in the chapter include funding review and revalidation, which ensures the integration of new data or information obtained after project approval; decision making regarding the timing of capital spending; handling of any budget deficits or surpluses; ongoing monitoring of project performance; and taking appropriate actions based on performance results.

Chapter Nine, "Making It Happen," describes how to establish the prerequisites for a successful implementation of a high-quality capital management process, namely education, communication, and a solid implementation plan with a realistic time frame. A detailed example of implementation of a best-practice process at a regional health system during a two-year period is provided. Finally, closing comments summarize the benefits of the rigorous corporate finance–based capital management approach recommended in this book.

CHAPTER ONE

Capital Allocation and Management Essentials

CAPITAL ALLOCATION IS defined as the strategic component of the capital management process used in organizations to make capital investment decisions. Through use of this process, healthcare executives determine how much capital will be invested and where the scarce capital resources will be deployed. A best-practice capital management process ensures that the organization spends the optimal amount of capital—not too much and not too little—and that investment is made in a portfolio of initiatives that provides a positive contribution to the organization's strategic and financial positions.

Capital Allocation and the Capital Management Cycle

Capital allocation is an integral component of the *capital management cycle*—an organic, circular pathway defining the flow of analysis and decision making related to the management of capital, as shown in Figure 1-1. A key concept of a corporate finance–based management philosophy, the capital management cycle starts with identification, through the *strategic planning process*, of market- and mission-based strategies that require funding. These strategies define the nature of the organization and the initiatives the organization wants and needs to pursue in the next five to ten years to achieve its objectives.

The next cycle stage, the *financial planning process*, is used in the organization to quantify the broad capital requirements and potential effects of the

I

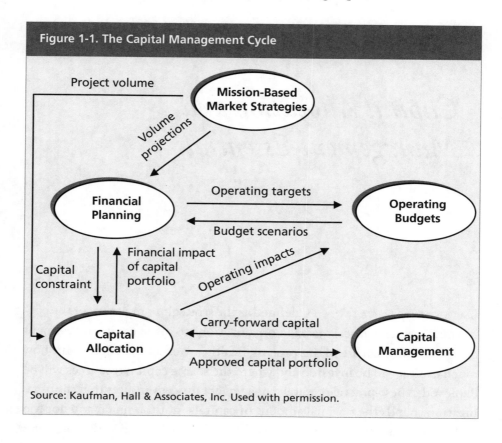

Figure 1-1. The Capital Management Cycle

Source: Kaufman, Hall & Associates, Inc. Used with permission.

defined strategies. The goal of financial planning is to evaluate whether the identified strategies can be implemented within an acceptable credit context. In conjunction with the financial plan, *capital structure management* focuses on optimizing the use of debt to fund the identified strategies in a manner that ensures maximum flexibility and the lowest possible cost of capital.

The evaluation and prioritization of specific capital spending opportunities, which occurs through an organization's *capital allocation process*, is a further, iterative step in the capital management cycle. Capital allocation balances strategic opportunities with financial capabilities. It ensures that capital will be deployed to meet the organization's strategic imperatives while enhancing, on a portfolio basis, the organization's financial integrity.

The *annual budgeting process*, which creates a current-year implementation plan and budget, integrates the targets of strategic and financial plans with the specific investment decisions of the capital allocation process. The operating budget is a strategic document that reflects the operating plan for an organization's base business and implementation of the selected strategies. It also provides a means to monitor revenue, expense, and capital on an ongoing basis.

Capital allocation is thus integrally linked with the organization's strategic, financial, and capital planning processes and annual budgeting process, as described more fully in Chapter Two.

The key principle underlying successful capital management is as follows:

Financial performance must be sufficient to meet the cash flow requirements of the strategic plan and, at the same time, maintain or improve the financial integrity of the organization within an agreed-upon credit and risk context.

Not-for-profit healthcare executives vary in their awareness and application of this core principle. Data from a survey of member hospitals and health systems by The Governance Institute (2005) indicate that surveyed leaders do not universally view their capital allocation process as a central bridge between their strategic plan and annual operating budget. Executives who fail to see the interconnectedness of strategy and capital allocation are at significant risk of damaging their organizations' financial performance and continued financial integrity.

The Significance of Capital Allocation and Management

The most important financial decisions made each year by an organization's senior management and ratified by its board relate to how much capital to spend and on which projects and initiatives the dollars will be spent. The long-term success of a healthcare organization is highly dependent on the capital investment decisions it makes today. Every decision either adds to or reduces organizational value. Decisions to invest capital must increase the organization's value—its ability to generate capital for future projects, maintain or improve its creditworthiness, and accomplish its mission. For every investment that does not generate value, the organization must seek other ways to create the cash flow and return that should have been generated. The cumulative effect of incremental decisions determines the organization's overall success.

Organizations cannot shrink their way to success. Organizational leadership must act on the knowledge that growth and investment to create growth are the foundation for the organization's future. Strategic investments that protect or improve the organization's net cash flow stream must be part of the long-term strategic financial plan.

High-performing organizations give the formal allocation of capital a high priority because they understand that existing capital capacity, defined as the amount of debt and cash flow–based capital an organization is capable of generating and supporting, is a function of past performance. The creation and regeneration of capital capacity depend on the organization's continuing ability to make value-adding investment decisions.

New sources of cash flow are harder and harder to find. In an environment of constrained payment, scarce resources, and increased competition, the cost of making bad capital investment decisions can be severe. Consider what occurred during the early 1990s, when the leaders of Allegheny Health Education and Research Foundation continued to acquire hospitals and physician practices in spite of the fact that previously acquired entities were not performing as required for continued financial health. Or, consider the strategies pursued by many healthcare organizations in the 1990s. The large-scale purchases of physician practices, investments in health plan ownership, and entries into capitation contracts by hospitals effectively lowered healthcare credit industrywide, resulting in decreased access to capital and rapidly escalating market consolidation.

Uninformed or poorly analyzed decisions made today often have financial and market effects that emerge three, five, or even ten years later. Such decisions reduce the organization's capital capacity, limiting the organization's ability to pursue future initiatives. In turn, this reduces the organization's ability to achieve or maintain competitive market strength. The effect is a compounded one.

The safety net provided in the past by Medicare and Medicaid cost reimbursement and generous indemnity insurance structures no longer exists. Credit markets have tightened, and the industry's operating cash flow and access to affordable capital are constantly challenged. To survive and succeed in the current environment, an organization's capital management process must be based on principles of corporate finance, involving rigorous and consistent application of solid decision criteria and proven quantitative techniques. These principles will be fully described later in the book.

Capital Management Is Not Capital Budgeting

Capital budgeting is the administrative process organizations use to spend capital that has been allocated. Capital budgeting is a small portion of the comprehensive capital management process. It often relates only to what are called "routine capital items," such as minor replacements that fall under department managers' purview.

Capital budgeting, more appropriately referred to as capital monitoring, involves the detailed listing and monitoring of purchases that will be made by departments during the next fiscal year. A capital budget provides a one-year look at expenditures. It does not provide a longer-term view of the combined impact of approved projects on cash flow, cash reserves, and the overall balance sheet.

Capital budgeting is an administratively driven process. Its success is measured by such criteria as "time required for completion" and "variance of proposed expenses from budget." Strategic and broader financial concerns are seldom included among the success indicators for capital budgeting, and rigorous analysis and strategic evaluation are often lacking.

In contrast, the success of a capital management process is directly tied to the organization's strategic financial performance. Available dollars are derived on the basis of the organization's long-term strategic and financial vision. Approved allocations of capital are designed to create an overall portfolio that will generate an optimal return over a multiyear period.

Unlike the one-year focus of a capital budgeting process, capital management comprehensively considers the short-term and long-term implications of each potential investment within an overall portfolio of investments. The focus often extends three to five years and, in the case of new facility development or new programs and services, for example, can extend a decade or more. The detailed analyses that support each particular capital investment proposal enable executives to identify and track key opportunities and risks. Problems related to individual project or portfolio performance can be corrected, or in the worst case, exit strategies can be devised before strategic financial performance is materially and negatively affected.

Common Approaches to Allocating Capital

Approaches to the actual allocation of capital vary considerably in contemporary healthcare organizations. A brief look at a number of common approaches, which are not best-practice or recommended, is often instructive.

First Come–First Served Approach

Perhaps the most prevalent approach to allocating capital in healthcare is the first come–first served approach. In hospitals and health systems using this approach, specific projects are evaluated in a serial fashion as they arise throughout the calendar year. The approach is, in fact, more of a project-approval process than a process for allocating capital.

Organizations employing this approach often go to great lengths to calculate the total amount of available capital to be spent, which is indeed a best-practice component of the recommended capital management approach. However, because of the serial nature of initiative evaluation and approval, the organization is not able to construct a portfolio of investments with the best strategic financial return. As the fiscal year progresses and projects are approved, capital is apportioned. Midway through the year, or even earlier, the capital needed to fund a project or projects capable of bringing significant growth to the organization may no longer be available.

For example, assume that the leaders of an organization have $10 million to allocate to projects during a one-year period. Project A, costing $4 million, is proposed in February, looks good, and is approved. Project B, costing $3 million, is proposed in March, looks acceptable, and is approved. Then Project C arrives in June. It has the best projected return of all three projects and is associated with a key strategic initiative, but it carries a $5 million price tag. Having already spent $7 million on Projects A and B, the organization simply does not have the funds for Project C. Management is faced with a devil's alternative. Had all three projects been evaluated simultaneously, the leaders would have decided to pursue Projects A and C, and hold off on B. Now the available options are to either forego a strategic opportunity or use precious cash reserves to over fund capital during the current fiscal year. This situation occurs simply because the business plan for Project C took 60 days longer to prepare than did the plans for Projects A and B.

Subjective or Political Approach

Many not-for-profit hospitals and health systems historically have approached the allocation of capital on a subjective or political basis. The department, service, or other unit that demands the most gets the most. The problem? Squeaky wheels with newly applied capital grease do not always bring the best returns. By essentially ignoring quantitative evaluation, this approach assumes that the core business can generate sufficient cash flow on an ongoing basis to support investment initiatives that may not have acceptable returns. More often than not, this type of process exists in organizations with highly centralized decision making and a culture that uses allocation of capital to reward past behavior or to reward or appease a powerful political constituency.

History-Based Approach

Another approach organizations often use is to allocate capital according to what was allocated in the previous year. Under this history-based allocation approach, if a hospital's radiology department or a hospital in a multihospital system received $X million or X percent of the total capital dollars this year, it would expect to receive the same (and maybe even an increased number of dollars or a similar share) next year. The problem? In today's rapidly changing healthcare environment, past performance may not always be the best predictor of future results.

For example, as described earlier in the chapter, physician practice investments, prevalent in the late 1990s, created significant losses rather than expected profitability. Continued allocation of capital to such strategies that do not bring expected returns can result in deteriorating financial performance and leave more promising strategies on the table.

Balanced Scorecard Approach

Some healthcare organizations use a balanced scorecard approach, which intends to evaluate potential investments based on both quantitative and qualitative management issues. Decision criteria include, for example, whether various new initiatives would meet community needs or increase physician satisfaction. For example, if a proposed project is designed to meet the qualitative goal of enhancing physician satisfaction, the approach gives high marks to that particular criterion. No quantification is provided.

Corporate finance–based allocation of capital would force the analysis to go a step further and quantify the potential impact of increased satisfaction. Will greater physician satisfaction lead to an increased use of hospital services? If so, what revenue increases could be expected? Will ancillary utilization increase, and if so, by what amount? Clearly, the answers to these questions will often be estimates, but even estimates provide the organization with some measure of the investment's potential return. Qualitative factors must be properly quantified and evaluated within an overall context of performance.

An additional problem with the balanced scorecard approach is its formulaic use of multiple, weighted criteria that essentially codifies the subjectivity of the group that established the weightings. For example, if there are 10 criteria, it is possible that only 10 percent of the decision weighting would be assigned to financial return—one of the 10 criteria. No organization can survive in the long run if it consistently pursues a series of investment decisions that are strategically driven to the detriment (or ignorant) of the organization's financial position. Financial return must be weighted more than other criteria, and the portfolio of investments selected must bring a positive return.

Go-with-the-Flow Approach

The go-with-the-flow approach to allocation of capital involves no methodology and no articulated policy. This is "Zen budgeting." The organization tries to fund whatever comes along, without the benefit of an evaluative process. The problem here is that not to decide about how investment decisions will be made is in fact to decide, because the organization must default to some type of approach, such as a first come–first served, a politics-driven process, or a combination thereof.

Characteristics of a Best-Practice Process

The recommended approach for allocating capital in healthcare organizations should be no different than the approach used by many *Fortune* 500 corporations. A best-practice approach has the following objectives:

- To support the mission and strategic goals of the organization
- To match capital expenditures to financial performance
- To protect and/or create capital capacity
- To provide uniform criteria for project evaluation
- To maintain the highest possible bond rating (i.e., optimal access to capital)
- To ensure consistent investment in the highest-performing assets

Structurally, best-practice capital management is founded on the following key elements:

- A high level of governance, education, and communication
- A coordinated calendar and planning cycle
- Direct links to a sound strategic financial plan
- Clear definitions of available capital and capital expenditures
- Rigorous, quantified, consistent business planning for each investment opportunity
- A standardized, one-batch review of potential investments
- Consistent application of quantitative analysis using corporate finance–based techniques
- Data-driven and team-based decision making
- Real post-approval project monitoring and measurement

These characteristics, which shape the contents of the rest of this book, are evident at many individual hospitals and health systems nationwide. A recent survey of capital management approaches employed by 26 health systems of varying size and location indicates that most system processes have similar characteristics, with some variation to meet organizational and cultural characteristics (Sussman 2005). Rigor, discipline, and standardization, however, were present in all systems that considered their capital management process to be successful.

Capital Resources Defined

A corporate finance approach to capital management is based on a contemporary definition of capital. This definition extends beyond traditional capital items, such as property, plant, and equipment, to embrace everything that might appear on the cash flow statement, including such items as working capital for investment start-ups, joint venture investments, and all other items that take cash out of the organization.

The standard definition of capital that focuses only on depreciable assets is far too narrow to support truly strategic capital management. Because of the breadth of sources for the capital deployed through the capital management process and the variety of uses for capital, a broad definition of capital must be a part of the basic structure of the capital management process. Sidebar 1-1 provides a broader, state-of-the-art definition of capital that could apply to a typical community hospital as easily as to a sophisticated regional provider or multihospital health system.

The capital management process apportions comprehensive organizational capital resources from the following sources:

1. Cash flow from operations
2. Philanthropy
3. External debt

As the state-of-the-art definition implies, best-practice capital management has widespread implications for the organization's decision making across the capital management cycle, including the following:

• Support for the organization's mission and community-based imperatives

> **Sidebar 1-1. Types of Investments Covered by the Capital Management Process**
>
> - Facilities
> - Property
> - Equipment
> - Business acquisitions and partnerships
> - Network development
> - Managed care investments
> - Program start-up subsidies/recruitment
> - Information technology
>
> Source: Kaufman, Hall & Associates, Inc. Used with permission.

- Strategic investment in existing service line growth and/or new businesses and ventures
- Ongoing infrastructure investment in the organization's property, plant, and equipment
- Major and long-term infrastructure investments, such as renovations and new facilities
- Retention or increase of balance-sheet cash reserves to fund liquidity levels consistent with optimal access to capital.

A best-practice capital management approach must have structured, high-quality governance and be understood broadly within the organization. These attributes can be achieved only through focused process design, which is the subject of Chapter Two.

References

Sussman, J. H. 2005. *Survey of Capital Allocation Approaches in 26 U.S. Health Systems*. Skokie, IL: Kaufman, Hall & Associates, Inc.

The Governance Institute. 2005. "New Rigor and Criteria: The Board's Role in Allocating Capital." *BoardRoom Press Newsletter* 16 (4): S1–S8.

CHAPTER TWO

Constructing a Best-Practice Capital Management Framework

THIS CHAPTER PROVIDES guidance on how to construct a framework that will support a best-practice capital management process. There are many common challenges to framework development and application. A description of several challenges follows.

Common Challenges

The first challenge is that some executives and readers of this book may conclude that their organizations already employ several or many of the best-practice components, and they will likely be correct. Healthcare organizations generally benefit from high-quality performance related to certain best-practice components, such as project-based decision making. Their designated capital committees meet frequently to review proposals for individual capital projects. These committees have devised organization-specific approaches to review and approval, whether based on years of standard practice, the personality of leaders, or the organization's perceived financial strength.

Notwithstanding the application of *selected* best practice components, creation of a best-practice capital management process requires *comprehensive* implementation of *all* of the key components.

For example, the annual review and allocation of capital using a single-batch approach is one best-practice component to be discussed in Chapter Six. Even if an organization has the best analytics in the world, without use of a single-batch approach, the organization can make the mistake of approving a mediocre but reasonable project in the first quarter of the year, only to find itself without capital resources to invest in a more deserving opportunity in the third quarter. Furthermore, the organization can never really know if it has made a good set of capital decisions on a fiscal-year basis.

A second common challenge is that the personality of leaders can prevent development and implementation of a best-practice capital management process. Constituencies with "skin in the capital game" include every internal and external interest group—physicians, patients, board members, community members, department managers, the government, and third-party payers. It is no wonder that some chief executive officers (CEOs) find it easier to simply make unilateral capital decisions than deal with the politics of the process. In doing so, however, these CEOs only exacerbate organizational politics while defining themselves as the lightning rods of consequences of the decisions made—good *and* bad.

The perceived financial strength of the organization is perhaps the most pernicious of the common challenges to an organization's use of a best-practice capital management process. Leaders of cash-rich organizations may believe that capital spending constraints are not needed. This perception, whether because of complacency or lack of focus, leaves many otherwise high-performing organizations extremely vulnerable strategically and financially. Over several fiscal years, poor capital decision making can transform a cash-rich hospital with high credit ratings to a cash-poor hospital with a lowered credit rating and significant pressure to rebuild its balance sheet while also trying to find dollars to pursue strategic capital needs.

Framework Basics

Best-practice capital management involves the application of a structured, rigorous, and disciplined business process to ensure that the organization remains focused on its true mission and vision. Through this process, capital decision making becomes an organizational function rather than being vested in one or a few senior executives. Availability of capital is driven objectively and formulaically, not based on subjective management decisions.

Implementation of a comprehensive process often involves substantial organizational change. As such, process development requires a strong foundation, which must be established by an organization's board of directors and senior executives. The foundation includes four elements: objectives, principles, process governance, and calendar-driven planning and decision making. Descriptions of these building blocks follow.

Objectives

The first building block is the development and implementation by leadership of formal, clearly articulated, and broadly communicated objectives or requirements for the process. The objectives may be part of a larger policy statement or appear as a separate document.

At the highest level, an organization's statement of objectives establishes the need for the process design to achieve the following:

- Consistency
- Standardization
- Reliance on analytics
- Known timing
- Transparency of governance and decision making

Sidebar 2-1 provides sample objectives from capital management processes that were successfully implemented in hospitals and health systems nationwide. Some of these objectives appear to be overly obvious and not deserving of articulation—for example, "align the long-range strategic, financial, and related operating plans of the organization." However, step back and consider the impact of flavor-of-the-month capital decisions made by healthcare organizations in past decades, such as investment in health plans that had little or no connection to core organizational mission and values. As obvious as this objective may be, its articulation is required.

Sidebar 2-1. The Objectives of Best-Practice Capital Management

- Provide rational and consistent guidelines for investment decisions.
- Develop uniform criteria and a formal review process for evaluating all investment decisions.
- Align the long-range strategic, financial, and related operating plans of the organization.
- Ensure that the portfolio of major investment decisions will add measurable financial and strategic value to the organization.
- Integrate the financial requirements of the capital management process and operating impacts of approved capital expenditures with the annual budget and multiyear financial plan.
- Enhance the financial strength and integrity of the organization by increasing its capital capacity and maintaining or improving its credit rating.
- Delineate clear roles, responsibilities, and accountability related to capital management and investment throughout the organization.

Source: Kaufman, Hall & Associates, Inc. Used with permission.

The objective to "ensure that the portfolio of major investment decisions will add measurable financial and strategic value to the organization" introduces two key best-practice requirements. The first is to create a portfolio of capital decisions, which by definition requires evaluation of multiple, competing opportunities at the same time, *not* in a serial manner over a number of months. For many organizations, this represents a fundamental process change.

The second best-practice fundamental introduced in this objective is the requirement for the organization to connect the strategic evaluation of potential opportunities with their financial evaluation. Organizations cannot make valid decisions in a strategic vacuum based solely on potential financial returns. Conversely, project decision making cannot be based on strategic implications of the selected projects without an evaluation of their related financial implications.

This simple objective establishes the imperative for integrated strategic financial planning and analysis, one of the most important attributes of a well-designed capital management process.

Principles

To ensure that the capital management process reflects the organization's core values, a set of principles should be established that will govern the design, implementation, and ongoing operation of the process. The principles provide guidance on how the process will achieve the established objectives. They answer such questions as how do executives ensure that the process design appropriately incorporates the portfolio concept? What mechanisms will ensure that individual projects and portfolios of projects benefit from integrated strategic financial analyses? Such principles must be articulated and agreed upon up front by the governing body.

Sidebar 2-2 provides a selected list of principles that have been developed and used by organizations with some of the most successful capital management processes in healthcare today. A description of the categories of principles follows.

Equal Access to Dollars

The first principle in this category states that all cash generated within the organization will be consolidated and available to meet all needs within the organization and its component entities.

For multihospital health systems, which include hospitals and other entities that generate differing levels of capital, this is a key, if not *the* most important, principle. Entities that produce more of the capital may want an approach that allocates capital based on contribution to the total dollars available for spending. However, this first best-practice principle holds that *where* the cash flow is generated should not drive access to capital. The guiding rationale is as follows:

> We are a system, and all dollars generated within the system should be managed for the system as a whole.

For community hospitals, this means that all departments, programs, or services within the hospital will have equal access to available dollars.

Sidebar 2-2. Capital Management Process Principles

Equal Access to Dollars
- Cash flow generated throughout the organization will be available to fund projects associated with any entity within the organization.
- All projects will be considered candidates for available funds.

Standardized Analytics, One-Batch Review, and Portfolio Decision Making
- The process for allocating capital is based on the assumption that the strategic and financial benefits of any capital investment can be quantified and articulated.
- All capital projects will be submitted in one-batch evaluation annually, with certain limited provisions for unforeseen emergency and off-cycle requests.
- Project evaluation will be completed without regard to anticipated funding or financing source.
- Some projects could project negative net present values. Over time, however, all projects in the aggregate should have a positive net present value.
- Funds available for capital requests below a certain dollar threshold will be allocated on a consistent, formulaic basis. Review and approval of those requests will be decentralized to the operating entities.

A Governed and Strategic Decision-Making Process
- The quality of the capital management process is directly related to the quality of the underlying preceding financial planning process. As such, financial plan development at the hospital and, for health systems, at the system level will receive the highest priority relative to the setting of appropriate financial goals and objectives and adherence to those goals and objectives.
- Major acquisitions will be evaluated based on their impact on the long-range strategic plan and financial goals of the organization.
- Capital capacity is based on historical results, and future capital capacity is generated through the success of current projects.
- Capital requests above a certain dollar threshold will be reviewed for projected financial performance, strategic importance, and relevance to the mission and strategies of the organization. Investment decisions and subsequent project performance will be measured and balanced to ensure the ongoing financial strength of the organization. Actual project results will be measured against projections to ensure the integrity of the approach to allocating capital and the transfer of knowledge related to project success or failure.

(Continued)

> ### Sidebar 2-2. Capital Management Process Principles (cont.)
>
> • Unspent proceeds for an approved threshold project can-not be transferred to another threshold or nonthreshold project, but rather they are returned to the general pool of funds for reallocation by the capital management governance group.
>
> Source: Kaufman, Hall & Associates, Inc. Used with permission.

Projects originating in departments that do not typically generate high revenues will have equal access to the total dollars available for spending.

The second principle in this category states that all projects must be considered candidates for available funds. Even though a facility in a health system or department in a community hospital may be losing money, its proposed projects will be considered. Allocation decisions are based on the fit of a potential project with the organization's strategic plan and the project's individual merits, not necessarily on past or present performance of the recommending entity.

Standardized Analytics, One-Batch Review, and Portfolio Decision Making

The principles in this category revolve around the understanding that standardized quantification of the potential costs and benefits of investment opportunities, as well as review of all projects as a portfolio of opportunities at one point in time, are critical to high-quality decision making. Informed decisions are data-driven decisions. As noted in the key principle in this category, the capital management process is based on the assumption that the strategic and financial benefits of any capital investment can be quantified.

Standardized analytics using templates or uniform formats ensure true comparability of projects and decision-making transparency. Although a capital management governance group could theoretically still make a subjective decision when following an apples-to-apples comparison of projects, this is much less likely to occur because other managers in the organization will be knowledgeable about the strategic and financial impact of selected investments.

The benefits of one-batch, one-time-per-year allocation of capital are significant and relate to governance of the process, control of total capital dollars spent, and enhanced ability of management to ensure consistency of capital investments with overall strategic direction. When dollars are allocated on an ongoing, serial basis, the approval process occurs piecemeal as well. The result is often approval of projects that compete strategically or create an unacceptable overall risk profile for the organization. Serial decision making increases the risk that the capital management process will be a political one.

One-batch capital allocation and portfolio management may represent a fundamental change in the way many organizations manage capital. Executives and managers may not be accustomed to presenting all of their projects at one point in time each year. Thus, one common objection from managers when a best-practice process is implemented at a hospital or health system revolves around having to wait for review of projects, for perhaps up to a full year. A response to such concern is to describe how one-batch allocation enables the organization to look at the big picture, thereby actually opening up the field to projects that might not see the light of day if considered separately.

For example, perhaps the organization has identified and tentatively selected six initiatives that are expected to generate a solid financial return as a portfolio of projects. The total anticipated return may actually be strong enough to enable the organization to also include in the portfolio a seventh or eighth project that will contribute significantly to meeting community needs but will not bring the level of return projected for the other six projects.

The big-picture perspective provided by portfolio decision making also enables organizations to review whether the projects in the portfolio represent the right mix from a strategic or market standpoint. For example, an organization might have established the strategic objective of increasing consumer access through development of outpatient facilities in specific geographic markets. Prior to decision making, review of selected projects might indicate that most, if not all, anticipated capital spending is on hospital-campus infrastructure or initiatives in only one market. Thus, there is a disconnect between established, agreed-upon strategy and actual implementation through the capital management process. Portfolio review enables organizations to ensure that they are pursuing initiatives that will advance their strategic plan. In this example, the portfolio of capital initiatives could easily be reconfigured to more consistently address the organization's strategic imperatives. This would *not* be the case if capital decisions are made serially rather than on a portfolio basis.

A Governed and Strategic Decision-Making Process

The principles in this category establish the strategic nature of the approach to allocating capital and the integral connection between the strategic and financial planning processes and the capital management process, as described in Chapter One. Without development of a strategic plan and the financial plan that quantifies the capital requirements and potential effects of the defined strategies, the organization will not be able to determine which capital investment opportunities should be pursued.

Process governance, as described in the next section, ensures that decisions are made in a best-practice manner and that selected initiatives are implemented, monitored, and measured against projections. As described fully in Chapter Eight, when the capital required for an approved project is less than originally anticipated, unspent proceeds are returned to the general pool of funds for reallocation by the governance group.

Process Governance

Governance is the linchpin to the ongoing consistency, integrity, and success of a capital management process. Articulated objectives and principles establish the foundation for a high-quality process; design of the governance structure is among the first implementation decisions on those objectives and principles. The governance structure in place must be consistent with the established framework.

Process Design

To identify the most appropriate governance structure, a task force that includes a broad range of the organization's management constituents is often created and given the mandate to design or redesign the capital management process. The task force should be charged with reviewing the existing approach to capital management; assessing its strengths and weaknesses; and defining a truly objective, structured process.

The task force should not include board members—given that allocating capital is a management process—and does not necessarily need to be composed of the same executives who ultimately will make up the capital management governance group. It may be more productive, in fact, if task force membership is based on organizational knowledge and technical capability. Members should bring to the design effort practical knowledge of existing systems and processes, including financial management, materials management, operations, clinical management, technology management, and strategic decision-making processes and capabilities.

In multihospital systems, the design task force should include representatives who can bring both corporate and operating-entity perspectives. In any organization, it is important to include a task force member who will encourage focus on the organization's mission, vision, and values.

The job of the design task force is formidable—it is truly one of organizational change. Creating the right process governance structure with the right participants is vital.

Governance Structure

Successful implementation of a best-practice process depends on the clear definition of process roles, responsibilities, and accountabilities. Although governance structures will vary by organization, it is imperative that governance involve high-level corporate and operational management. By definition, managing capital is a process that involves money; through the distribution of dollars, the process also apportions organizational influence and power.

In establishing the governance structure, the task force should consider the following questions:

- Should governance be exclusively composed of senior or corporate management?

- What role should be played by constituencies such as medical staff and operating-entity managers?
- Who will/will not have voting privileges?
- How often should the capital management governance group meet?
- Will middle management interact with the governance group? If so, how?
- What process steps and tasks should the governance group delegate, and to whom?

With so much at stake, process governance must be completely supported by the CEO. Even if the CEO decides not to actively participate in the governance structure (hereafter called the capital management council, or council), it should be absolutely clear that the CEO is working in close partnership with the chief financial officer (CFO) to affect this key decision-making process change. The CEO's unconditional support and leadership help ensure a level playing field among senior executives and avoid process runarounds, which are more likely to occur without such leadership.

The capital management council should be heavily weighted toward corporate (organization-wide) representation. The decisions that this group will make will have significant strategic and financial consequences for the entire organization, not just one constituency or entity. Selection of one initiative over another represents an explicit articulation of the organization's long-term direction. If the structure that governs and drives such decisions is fraught with political infighting or favors one constituency over another, it becomes virtually impossible for appropriate, strategic decisions to be made on a consistent basis.

Sidebar 2-3 provides a suggested governance structure. The group should include key members of the C-suite—for example, the CEO, CFO, chief operating officer (COO), chief information officer (CIO), and chief medical officer (CMO)—and operational executives. In a multihospital system, the operational executives would typically be CEOs of subsidiary entities or regional executives. In an academic medical center, the operational executives may include representatives from the faculty practice plan and the academic departments. In a community hospital, vice president–level executives responsible for major operating components may be included as voting members of the governance group.

> **Sidebar 2-3. Capital Management Governance Structure**
>
> **Voting Members**
> - Chief executive officer
> - Chief operating officer
> - Chief financial officer
> - Chief information officer
> - Chief medical officer
> - Operational representatives (2–3 members)
>
> **Nonvoting Staff Support**
> - Finance staff
> - Strategic planning staff
> - Information systems staff
>
> Source: Kaufman, Hall & Associates, Inc. Used with permission.

Some hospitals and health systems include their CIO or lead information systems executive as a voting member of the council; others ensure integration of the CIO's input into the process but, because of the size and scope of information technology (IT) investments, do not extend voting privileges to CIOs.

At a minimum, council participation by operational executives is vital to successful implementation of a best-practice capital management process. These management team members will be responsible for the successful implementation of initiatives selected through the process. Their participation provides them with a broader organizational/system view of capital-related decision making and also facilitates the direct transfer of knowledge regarding strategic issues and the success or failure of selected initiatives.

In addition, participation of operational executives in the peer project review, as required of best-practice capital management, increases process transparency. Peers know the questions to ask and will not accept incomplete or unsound responses from colleagues. They can accurately assess the scarcity of resources and make this information available to peers and their departments. Their participation in post-allocation review of approved projects, as described in Chapter Eight, ultimately forces more credible up-front project analysis. However, when participating on the capital management council, operational executives must understand that they are acting as organizational, not constituency, representatives. A well-designed process will reinforce this requirement through the transparency and visibility of the decision-making process.

Following is a description of sample governance structures at a community hospital, a two-hospital health system, and a larger health system.

Community Hospital. The capital management council of a community hospital has both voting and nonvoting members. Voting members include the CEO, COO, CFO, CMO, and chief nursing officer (CNO). Nonvoting members include the CIO and staff from finance, business development/strategic planning, human resources, facilities management, and clinical support. The CIO, whose capital spending historically has been as extensive as that of the director of the radiology department, is not extended voting privileges to minimize potential conflicts of interest.

Market-Based Health System. A two-hospital system located in a single market has a multidisciplinary capital management council composed of senior leaders who participate in all aspects of the integrated strategic financial planning and capital management processes. The team includes the CEO, COO, CFO, CNO, CIO, medical directors of the hospitals, and the director of ambulatory facilities. In this organization, the CIO coordinates IT-related initiatives, validating their strategic importance and operational appropriateness. Because the CIO does not specifically propose initiatives, the CIO has voting privileges and provides the council with a vital objective and informed perspective. Support staff to the council is much broader in a health system than in many other organizations, and includes the director of facilities management and vice presidents of operations, strategic planning, and finance. Given the organization's breadth of activities, the council requires access to a wider range of experts to support its decision making.

Multihospital System. The voting members of the multidisciplinary governance group of an 11-hospital system includes the executive vice president of hospital operations, senior vice president of regional hospital operations, system CFO, an urban-hospital CEO, a regional hospital CEO, the senior vice president of ambulatory services, and the medical director. This structure provides widespread expertise as well as broad-based representation of the full range of constituencies within the system. Support for the governance group is coordinated by key corporate finance staff, but the group accesses expertise throughout the system to address specific issues generated by various initiatives.

A recent survey of health systems suggests that governance of the capital management process varies considerably by system type (Sussman 2005). The survey also indicates that there is an inverse relationship between centralized authority and governance and system size and market breadth (see Figure 2-1).

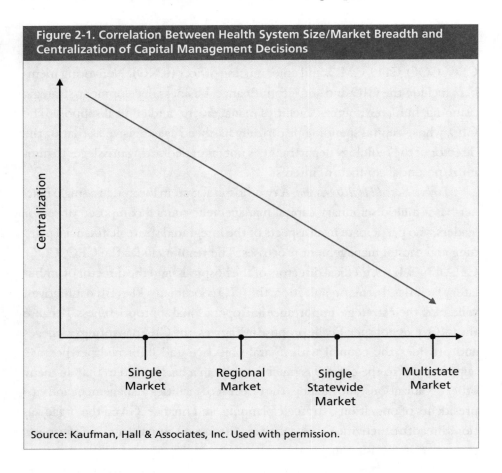

Figure 2-1. Correlation Between Health System Size/Market Breadth and Centralization of Capital Management Decisions

Source: Kaufman, Hall & Associates, Inc. Used with permission.

In multistate, multimarket systems, decision-making authority is often *decentralized*. Regional executives and/or executives of the organizations within the system that are market leaders assume significant decision-making authority. This is clearly a function of organizational culture and the maturity of the capital management process in multistate, multimarket health systems.

Large, multihospital systems, especially Catholic hospital systems, have been at the forefront of design and implementation of corporate finance–based approaches to managing capital. This probably reflects the fact that capital management issues are typically more material in large systems — the dollars are bigger, the number of requests is more varied and numerous, and the ability to control investment of strategic capital is more diffuse. These factors have compelled large multihospital systems to address capital management in a manner similar to that in a *Fortune* 100 company, such as GE. Their capital decision processes are highly decentralized, rely heavily on standardized analytic techniques, and involve the rigorous application of decision-making criteria throughout the organization.

In contrast, decision-making authority in stand-alone community hospitals and small health systems operating in a single market tends to be highly centralized in the C-suite. This reflects less about the technical capabilities of senior executives at these organizations and more about the ability (perhaps, the desire) of the CEO and senior management to be involved in the project development process from A to Z. The effect of such involvement is highly variable. In some instances, senior management makes project decisions following extensive and thoughtful analyses. In other situations, however, senior management uses political sway to gain approval of capital initiatives that otherwise would have been denied.

Regardless of the level of centralization of decision making, corporate management representation is one constant in the process governance structure of all types of healthcare organizations. According to the survey cited earlier, all organizations also require central approval for high-dollar projects, although the dollar level defined as "high" varies considerably.

Calendar-Driven Planning and Decision Making

After establishing the structural framework for decision making and governance, organizations need to create an environment that can foster comprehensive capital decision making. Effective allocation of capital requires coordination between the organization's strategic, financial, and capital planning and its capital management and budgeting processes. The timing and structure for these processes should reflect their interdependent nature and be rigorously observed.

Integrated and Portfolio-Based Planning

The process of managing capital is ultimately a function of an organization's culture. An organization with a planning culture uses capital allocation and management as the means to implement strategies and initiatives defined and developed through its annual planning processes.

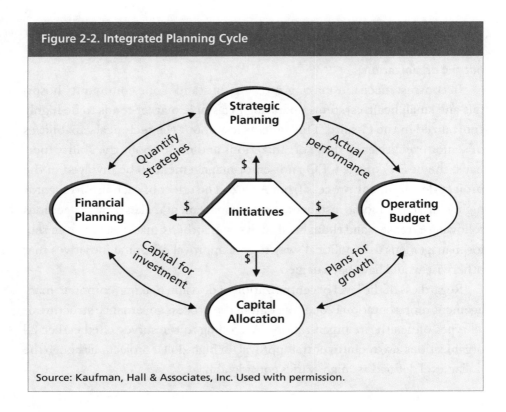

Figure 2-2. Integrated Planning Cycle

Strategic Planning

Quantify strategies

Actual performance

Financial Planning

Initiatives

Operating Budget

Capital for investment

Plans for growth

Capital Allocation

Source: Kaufman, Hall & Associates, Inc. Used with permission.

An integrated planning cycle ensures that strategic planning is completed within the context of the organization's financial capabilities and that initiatives are comprehensively analyzed from both strategic and financial contexts. Annual financial planning identifies the required levels of financial performance that ensure funding of selected strategies while maintaining or improving the financial position of the organization at a given level of capital access and risk. The financial plan results then drive the targets for the annual operating budget and define the levels of capital available for allocation (see Figure 2-2).

This type of planning requires an integrated and disciplined approach to capital management that relies, ultimately, on a rigorous portfolio approach to decision making. Sidebar 2-4 outlines typical portfolio-based questions that should be asked and answered as part of the integrated planning approach. Strategy-based questions establish the organization's investment direction, defining the parts of its portfolio (the markets and/or service lines) targeted for new investment, growth, maintenance, or divestiture. Finance-based questions

Sidebar 2-4. Issues of Strategic Portfolio Management

Strategy-Based Issues

- Should we continue to operate all of our current markets/service lines?
- In which markets/service lines should we invest heavily? In which should we invest at a level to maintain? In which should we reduce investment or divest?
- Are there new market/service-line investments required to meet our strategic goals for growth?

Finance-Based Issues

- What level of overall return is required from our investment in strategic capital?
- What is the projected return of the selected portfolio?
- How do changes in the mix of allocated capital affect the overall portfolio return?
- What are the cash flow implications of the proposed portfolio of strategic capital investment?

Source: Kaufman, Hall & Associates, Inc. Used with permission.

quantify the implications of investment in the strategic portfolio. Through the portfolio view, management is able to evaluate on a comprehensive basis the potential for its strategic capital investments to generate short-term and long-term value to the organization.

The goal of integrated planning is to understand and evaluate the complete impact of the organization's strategic capital investments. Portfolio analysis requires a process that allocates capital on an annual basis rather than on a serial basis throughout the year. By batching all of its initiatives together, an organization's management can fully assess the return on investment and annual cash flow requirements of an entire strategic portfolio, and create the portfolio that optimizes risk versus return for the organization. A portfolio approach supports the development and implementation of operating budgets that are designed to implement the organization's selected strategies.

The best-practice capital decision-making calendar segregates the fiscal year into two major components of roughly six months each. The first component is the planning component during which the organization updates and challenges its assessment of its market and financial positions. The second component uses the analysis and targets established during the planning component to create annual operating and capital plans focused on implementing the defined strategies.

The Planning Component: From Strategic Planning to Financial Planning

Because of its inherent scarcity, capital must be allocated on the basis of a sound strategic financial plan, which includes good ideas worthy of investment. If the ideas articulated in the plan will not generate the incremental cash flow needed to support the performance requirements of the plan, the management team should either go back to the drawing board and identify ideas that will do so or consider alternatives, such as joint ventures and acquisitions, to meet the organization's mission while achieving competitive financial performance.

Strategic analysis, including detailed market and competitive assessments, can and should occur throughout the year, but the strategic financial plan update must happen at one point in time to initiate the year's planning process. The annual update of the strategic plan provides the starting point for understanding the organization's long-term market objectives and the related strategic capital requirements necessary to reach those objectives. The financial plan quantifies both how the initiatives identified in the strategic plan update will affect overall volume, revenue, cost, and other financial indicators and what capital will be required to pursue those initiatives (Figure 2-3).

Through the real integration of the strategic and financial planning processes, management establishes the short-term and long-term profitability and cash flow targets that will enable the organization to fund its strategy over a specified period of time.

The Implementation Component: From Strategic Financial Planning to Capital Allocation and Budgeting

On the foundation established by the integrated strategic financial planning, organizations can develop and implement annual operating and capital

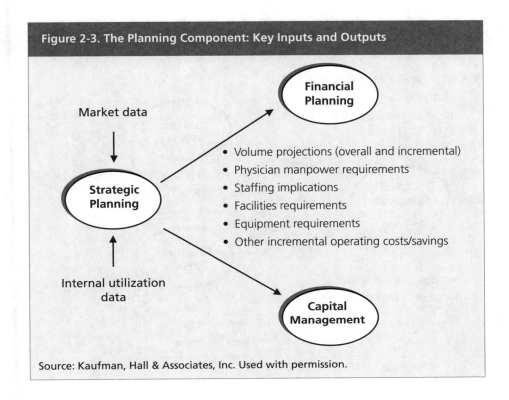

Figure 2-3. The Planning Component: Key Inputs and Outputs

Market data

Strategic Planning

Financial Planning

- Volume projections (overall and incremental)
- Physician manpower requirements
- Staffing implications
- Facilities requirements
- Equipment requirements
- Other incremental operating costs/savings

Internal utilization data

Capital Management

Source: Kaufman, Hall & Associates, Inc. Used with permission.

budgets. These budgets are essentially the annual implementation plans for the organization's strategy. The operating budget should be consistent with the first year of the financial plan. In that way, all constituencies understand that operating constraints of the budget are required to ensure the organization's continued ability to access capital to fund its strategies. The operating targets defined in the strategic financial plan also quantify the amount of cash flow available each year to fund capital. The first-year profitability and cash flow targets/projections from the planning process should be used to calculate the organization's annual capital constraint.

A best-practice capital management process begins with identification of the capital constraint, as described in Chapter Three. The *capital constraint* is the maximum amount of capital available to be spent by the organization in a given year, based on the organization's long-term strategic and financial goals. The capital constraint reflects key management decisions regarding the organization's overall debt structure, the level of required cash reserves, and the profitability required to sustain and enhance the

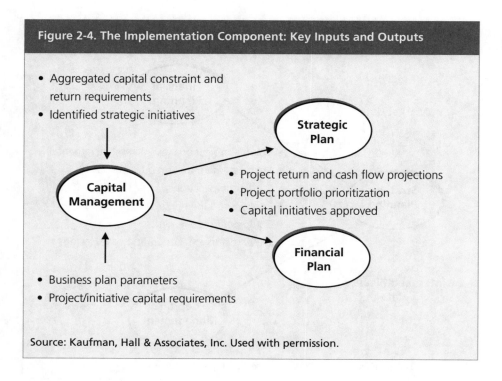

Figure 2-4. The Implementation Component: Key Inputs and Outputs

- Aggregated capital constraint and return requirements
- Identified strategic initiatives

Strategic Plan

Capital Management

- Project return and cash flow projections
- Project portfolio prioritization
- Capital initiatives approved

Financial Plan

- Business plan parameters
- Project/initiative capital requirements

Source: Kaufman, Hall & Associates, Inc. Used with permission.

organization's access to capital. Figure 2-4 illustrates key implementation inputs and outputs.

Putting It All Together

The beauty of a connected process (Figure 2-5) is best illustrated when senior executives ultimately go to the board for budget approval. Instead of having to field difficult questions regarding levels of profitability, capital, salaries, and other variables, senior executives are able to present an integrated package. Their presentation can be made as follows:

Here is our overall, *multiyear strategy,* including the specific strategic initiatives for the coming year. Based on that strategy, here is our *strategic financial plan* that has quantified the capital and operating requirements of the identified strategies; identified financial targets consistent with funding the

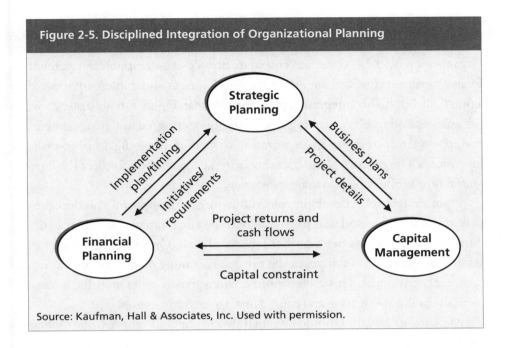

Figure 2-5. Disciplined Integration of Organizational Planning

Source: Kaufman, Hall & Associates, Inc. Used with permission.

strategy within the context of our organizational credit and risk parameters; and positioned us for ongoing, future strategic investment.

Finally, based on those long-term targets and requirements, here are our current-year *operating and capital budgets* that are consistent with the first year of the strategic financial plan, and thereby consistent with the strategic plan, which is consistent with our mission and values. The budgets include our *recommendations for investing capital* to implement that strategy. These capital recommendations fit within the budgeted cash flow and minimum cash reserve targets, consistent with our capital constraint as well as our short-term and long-term strategic financial plans.

Presentation of such an integrated package facilitates discussions with the board, rating agencies, and other capital market constituents, as appropriate, at a truly strategic level. It also provides a tool for senior executives and others to measure and monitor the success or failure of the various strategic and operating initiatives.

Ultimately, the integrated plan provides a finite and quantitative platform from which to launch next year's planning process.

An Integrated Calendar

Organizations with best-practice, corporate finance–based capital management focus significant time and energy on the development and implementation of a practical, but highly integrated, planning calendar. Figure 2-6 illustrates how the analysis and results of strategic planning, budgeting, capital management, and approval tie directly to an organization's overall and ongoing decision-making process. The process calendar, as shown in the figure, should reflect the integrated flow of the capital management cycle.

From strategic plan development to ultimate capital approval, this decision-making cycle takes a full year to complete. Typically, strategic planning occurs during the first three to five months of the fiscal cycle. Quantification and integration of identified initiatives in the financial planning process occurs during the next two months. This leaves approximately five to seven months to complete the annual budgeting and capital management processes.

Allocation of capital should be scheduled to conclude approximately one month before finalization of the annual operating budget. This enables management to incorporate projects that have been allocated capital and that have related operating impacts into the appropriate departmental operating budget for implementation.

Calendar Components

The typical order of events incorporated in an annual decision-making calendar is as follows:

- Strategic plan development/update
- Long-range financial plan development/update
- Establishment of profitability targets and the capital constraint
- Initiation of operating budget development
- Allocation of capital
- Finalization of current-year operating and capital budgets

The process of allocating capital must be an integral component of the organization's overall strategic and financial planning calendar. It should not

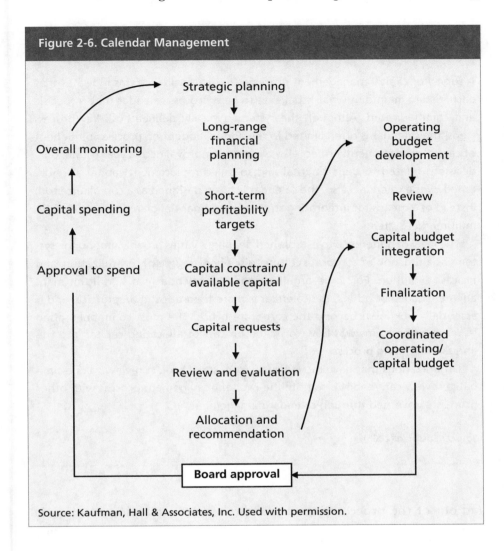

Figure 2-6. Calendar Management

Source: Kaufman, Hall & Associates, Inc. Used with permission.

be a stand-alone process or simply an add-on at the tail end of operating budget discussions. Organizations often try to devise a different flow for the process steps, for example, by providing revised strategic plans throughout the calendar year. However, this leads to serial project development and approval problems, such as those described in Chapter One related to the first come–first served approach to allocation.

The flow illustrated in Figure 2-6 is really the only process flow that works on a consistent basis to achieve superior results. Strict calendar management is vital to ensure that projects or initiatives do not slip in

---

Sidebar 2-5. Current Status of Calendar Management in Health Systems

A survey of capital management processes in healthcare systems indicates that each system maintains what it believes to be a process calendar that is specific and communicated. Although the systems typically delineate all key process steps, the calendar is often limited to the annual budgeting process component of capital management. Project allocation and approval occurs year round; only decisions related to departmental and so-called replacement capital are governed by the calendar. Also, the calendar is often designed as a compliance tool instead of a means for integrating strategic and financial planning, especially in multimarket systems.

The level of adherence to established deadlines varies broadly among the systems as a function of corporate culture, discipline, degree of centralization, and process evolution. For some organizations, the calendar is a significant management tool. For others, the calendar is more theoretical than practical and is essentially unknown beyond the corporate office. The most commonly raised issue among systems was how to fit the process of allocating capital into the annual budgeting process.

Organizations that have moved away from serial project review to one-time batch review can readily integrate the capital management process with other processes governed through calendar management.

Source: Sussman (2005).

---

and out of the process without comprehensive strategic and financial review.

Sidebar 2-5 outlines the current status of the use of a calendar approach at surveyed health systems. Suffice it to say that there is significant room for improvement.

Communicating and Maintaining the Calendar

To be truly effective, the calendar of decision-making events must be clearly defined, documented, and communicated throughout the organization. Communication should be ongoing, and all staff should be aware of the date when capital requests and related analyses are due and the date when projects are evaluated.

Submission dates for the analysis of large capital projects that exceed a dollar threshold defined by the organization—threshold capital projects, as described in Chapter Four—must be established well in advance with little to no tolerance for late submissions. If threshold capital analyses are not received by the specified date, executives and the capital management council should have the backbone to decline consideration of these projects until the following year. It generally takes only one or two such refusals for staff to understand that the dates are hard and nonnegotiable. When the council sticks to its guns, everyone enjoys definite and distinct benefits.

Calendar-Based Decision-Making Governance

The capital management council should meet at one specific time each year to evaluate capital investment opportunities and make capital allocation decisions for the year. The group should continue to meet quarterly to revalidate projects for purposes of approving funding, to monitor progress of funded initiatives, and to evaluate the need to release contingency funds for emergency or out-of-cycle needs. Review and approval timing for threshold capital requests must allow annual budget submissions to reflect departmental operating impacts of approved projects. These topics will be addressed fully in Chapters Five through Eight.

Monthly meetings of the council are unnecessary and unproductive, and they imply that allocation decisions can be made every month. This should not be the case. The monitoring of capital spending on a monthly basis should be part of the monthly budget review process. This should require variance explanations similar to what occurs with the operating budget. At its quarterly meetings, the council can review capital projects with variance issues.

Figure 2-7, Table 2-1, and Sidebar 2-6 provide sample detailed integrated planning schedules that incorporate key capital management activities. As discussed in Chapter Nine, hospitals and health systems might wish to consider making the transition to a calendar system over a multiyear period, because the scope of changes that may be required is often extensive.

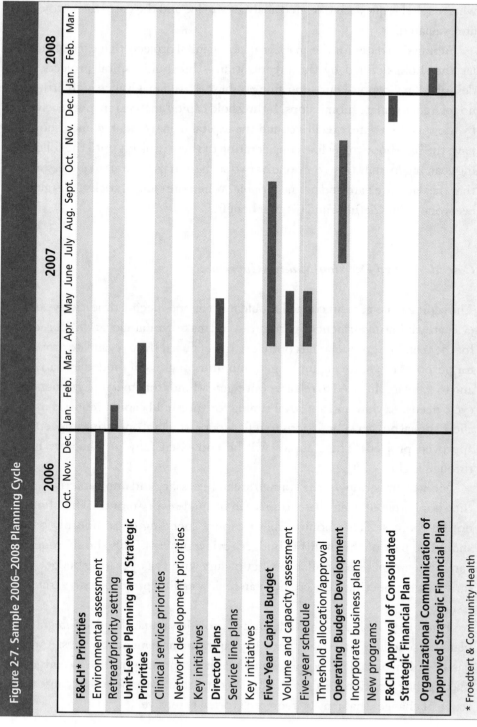

Figure 2-7. Sample 2006–2008 Planning Cycle

* Froedtert & Community Health

Source: Froedtert & Community Health, Milwaukee, WI. Used with permission.

Table 2-1. A Detailed, Integrated Planning Calendar

Task	July–June Fiscal Year
Strategic plan development/update	July to October
Distribution of capital project approval forms	September 15
Development of financial plan	November to January
Five-year targets established	January 31
Determination of capital constraint	February 1
Submission of nonthreshold requests	February
Allocation of funds to threshold and nonthreshold pools	February 1
Deadline for submission of project approval forms	February 15
Project approval review (including discussions)	February to March
Complete threshold review packages to capital management council	March 15
Capital management council meeting	March 31
Allocation of cash flow to threshold projects	March 31
Allocated projects incorporated into facility budget and financial plan	April
Preparation of annual budgets	April 30
Review of submitted budgets issue resolution	May
Leadership review and sign-off	May 31
Finance and audit committee approval of budgets	early June
Board approval of budgets	mid-June

Source: Kaufman, Hall & Associates, Inc. Used with permission.

In summary, an integrated calendar helps to ensure efficient, effective, and consistent decision making. Complete integration of planning processes supports seamless decision making.

Sidebar 2-6. Organizing for Calendar Management: An Example

To make the transition to an integrated calendar-management system, a two-hospital health system divided its fiscal year (a calendar year) into major management functional periods and assigned each calendar component to a specific council with corporate oversight as follows:

- *Market assessment,* which occurs in November and December—13 and 14 months ahead of the budget year—has oversight from a decision support council composed of key leaders in the market and decision support areas of each hospital.
- *Strategic planning,* which occurs from January through April, has oversight from a strategic planning council.
- *Financial planning,* which occurs from April through September, includes two stages: long-range financial planning, which involves a high-level assessment of the viability of the strategic plan, and identification of the profitability targets and the capital constraint (by June 15), followed by a detailed project-by-project analysis of plan elements and an overall portfolio analysis. Oversight is provided by the decision support council.
- *Capital allocation* culminates with allocation recommendations made to a capital management council on October 1, following the development and analysis of capital requests during the second and third quarters.
- *Operations and capital funding* commences with operating budget development during the third quarter, based on the short-term profitability targets identified during the financial planning process. The capital allocations approved on October 1 are integrated into the operating and capital budgets, finalized, and reviewed/approved by the board on November 15. Hospital/system management oversees this process.

Source: Kaufman, Hall & Associates, Inc. Used with permission.

Reference

Sussman, J. H. 2005. *Survey of Capital Allocation Approaches in 26 U.S. Health Systems.* Skokie, IL: Kaufman, Hall & Associates, Inc.

CHAPTER THREE

Determining the Capital Constraint

A BEST-PRACTICE capital management process is framed by a clear definition of the *capital constraint*, which is defined as the net capital available for spending during a designated period of time.

How much can the organization afford to spend on capital next year? How much can the organization afford for the next three to five years? This chapter addresses how organizations should answer these questions; but ultimately, the answers must be driven by the organization's long-range strategic financial plan. This plan should include operating, financial, and capital projections based on the organization's defined strategies. It should also reflect management decisions regarding the organization's targeted long-term financial structure and optimal access to capital.

Every organization faces a limitation on available capital resources. The specific limitation is determined by the organization's current level of operations, debt structure, and cash position. To make informed and timely decisions, the capital constraint must be well understood. Some organizations simply look at last year's spending levels or the income statement—for example, net income plus depreciation or a percentage of total operating revenue—as a starting point. Because this approach does not account for changes in the organization's balance sheet that require or provide cash, it provides an incomplete view of capital availability, which can lead to financially detrimental levels of capital spending. To be complete and reflect the net cash available for capital spending (i.e., the capital constraint) all sources and uses of funds, including principal payments, working capital changes, and additions to balance-sheet cash reserves, must be added to an income statement–based calculation.

The Mechanics

To determine an organization's capital constraint, financial leaders should start by asking the following simple question: What amount of capital, obtained both through internal operations and external sources, are we reasonably sure can be generated to support the organization's development over a defined period of time?

The answer to this question relates to how much the organization can and should borrow as well as the level of cash that it can generate and retain from operations in uncertain times. Cash available for capital spending will be a function of projected operating results, planned use of external debt, changes to the balance sheet, and projected levels of nonincome statement philanthropy (for example, capital campaign contributions).

Sidebar 3-1 outlines the basic components of the capital constraint. A more detailed look at each component follows.

Cash Flow

This component is the starting point for any calculation of capital availability and is often determined by the simple addition of income plus depreciation. However, whether income should reflect only income from operations or should include all nonoperating sources, such as investment income, contributions, and gains on sale of assets, can be a significant issue for an organization. A focus solely on operating income as the starting point creates an automatic reserve to increase balance sheet liquidity at the expense of current-year capital spending. This approach is often used by organizations with balance sheet weakness or a history of spending too much capital. On the other hand, including income from all sources maximizes current-year capital availability, but it increases the importance of

---

Sidebar 3-1. Components of the Capital Constraint

Cash Flow

Plus Total Sources of Cash	**Less Total Uses of Cash**
Debt proceeds	Working capital
Philanthropy	Principal payments
Other sources of cash	Carry-forward capital
Cash reserve requirements	Other uses of cash

= Total cash available for capital

Less Contingency

= Net cash available for capital allocation – the capital constraint

Source: Kaufman, Hall & Associates, Inc. Used with permission.

---

establishing and meeting the rigorous balance-sheet cash-reserve targets in the strategic financial plan.

Debt Proceeds

This capital constraint component includes proceeds from debt that will be issued in the upcoming year *and* the unspent but still available proceeds of debt issued in prior years. An organization should incur no more debt than is consistent with maintaining the credit rating that enables it to effectively compete in the marketplace and maintain optimal access to capital. The amount of debt the organization is capable of supporting within a particular desired credit-rating profile is its *debt capacity*.

Executives must conduct a rigorous debt capacity analysis before commencing their annual process for allocating capital. Typically, this analysis occurs as part of the organization's strategic financial planning process. A survey, however, indicates that less than 45 percent of healthcare trustees view debt capacity analysis as an important practice (The Governance Institute 2005). This is extremely problematic for the healthcare industry, especially given the importance of external sources of cash to the overall capitalization of most healthcare organizations.

Philanthropy

Many, if not most, not-for-profit healthcare organizations benefit from ongoing donations generated as a result of their community, academic, or religious affiliation. Such contributions appear as nonoperating revenue on their income statements. Depending on the definition of income adopted by the organization (see Cash Flow section earlier), this revenue stream may already be part of the capital constraint calculation.

Extraordinary philanthropy, which is typically associated with a particular capital initiative or a capital campaign, is the main focus of this capital constraint component. This source of cash flow often is not recorded as an income item, but flows directly to the balance sheet. Thus, the inclusion of such philanthropic funds in the calculation of the capital constraint is critical.

The availability of philanthropic dollars raises a number of questions. Should earmarked, donated funds be considered a capital source or be applied to reduce the cost of the specific project that attracted the funds? Within its overall capital management process, how should an organization handle specific-purpose contributions to an entity or program?

However executives choose to answer these questions, the key is to maintain transparency in the reporting of the flow of philanthropic dollars. These funds should be specifically identified as a source of cash, but at the same time should be designated as available only if the identified project is approved. Full disclosure of the total capital risk associated with a potential investment before approval and in the project monitoring stage is important. It is essential to both maintain the integrity of the gift and ensure that a high-quality investment decision is made about the associated project.

For example, a major teaching hospital recently received a donation for the development of an ambulatory center. The gift was large enough to cover the capital costs of the project, making the project essentially free from a net capital perspective. In some organizations, projects that do not involve a net capital allocation would not have to be reviewed by capital committees, so this project simply would have simply moved forward. This teaching hospital, however, required project review. The review revealed the fact that, while capital costs were covered by the generous contribution, projections indicated that the ambulatory center would operate at significant loss *ad infinitum*. Going ahead with this project could place the hospital at significant financial risk.

Working Capital

The income statement does not provide a complete picture of funding requirements. An organization that is growing, or one whose net current assets are growing, will have material year-to-year needs to fund working capital. These changes flow through the balance sheet and cash flow statement, but not through the income statement. An organization that uses a simple percentage-of-operating-income measure to calculate capital spending targets overlooks a potentially significant use (or source) of cash.

Principal Payments

In a similar vein, payments of principal on existing and new anticipated debt constitute direct uses of cash that are not accounted for on an organization's income statement. Depending on the amortization structure of the organization's outstanding debt, principal payments could have a material impact on cash available for capital.

For example, consider the small hospital that, because of limited access to the broader capital markets, has financed its major capital through use of vendor-provided capital leases or state-managed equipment-pool loans. These debt structures often have very short amortization periods, meaning that the organization may be repaying 15 percent to 20 percent of the asset value each year. Such substantial payments, while not reflected on the organization's income statement, effectively reduce the net cash available to the organization for capital. If these payments are not included in the capital constraint calculation, the organization could essentially create a capital constraint based on excessive spending and could severely damage the integrity of its balance sheet.

Carry-Forward Capital

In general terms, *carry-forward capital* can be defined as approved capital expenditures that have or will have a multiyear cash flow impact. Identifying and quantifying specific types and amounts of carry-forward capital are critical to an accurate capital constraint calculation.

As indicated in Sidebar 3-1, carry-forward capital should be a direct deduction from available cash flow. To determine carry-forward capital amounts, the organization must first establish firm definitions related to types of carry-forward capital. There are three basic types of carry-forward capital:

- *Type 1*: Capital dollars originally committed for approved capital projects with a planned, multiyear implementation schedule
- *Type 2*: Capital dollars required to complete an initiated approved project whose completion was originally anticipated to occur within the current fiscal year but will not occur until the subsequent fiscal year
- *Type 3*: Capital dollars allocated in the current year to projects or other types of capital requests whose implementation has not commenced at the end of the current fiscal year

After defining specific types of carry-forward capital, organizations should establish specific policies related to the funding of each type. This is critical to calculating and managing the current-year capital constraint and ensuring deployment of capital dollars according to the organization's strategic financial plan.

Every organization should address carry-forward capital issues in a manner consistent with its culture and structure. Type 3 carry-forward capital typically generates the most complex issues, including the following:

- The organization's ability to quantify the approved capital spending that has not yet been committed
- The impact of large carry-forward amounts on the organization's ability to support future capital initiatives
- The potential for creation of a use-it-or-lose-it attitude or approach
- The discipline and rigor of the organization's project management process

An objective evaluation of these issues will result in a policy associated with carry-forward capital that is, in all likelihood, unique to each organization. Examples of how other organizations have addressed these issues follow.

Example 1

A 250-bed community hospital determines net cash available for capital spending based on its long-range strategic financial plan, as described in this chapter. The hospital establishes the following parameters for carry-forward capital.

TYPE 1

Funding will be managed by the capital management council, which will receive project updates at the beginning of the subsequent years' capital management process. Updates will include information on the remaining capital to be spent on approved projects that are included in the capital constraint calculation. Previously approved and initiated projects may be placed on indefinite hold or terminated under extreme circumstances only (for example, financial deterioration or change of strategic direction).

TYPE 2

Funding will be managed by the capital management council on the basis of project updates received at the beginning of the subsequent years' capital management process. Based on the actual schedule, the council will reaffirm expected completion dates of those projects that have been initiated. Unspent capital from the current year will be carried forward to fund completion of the project unless the project is over budget. If the overrun exceeds a predefined budget-variance limit, the council will determine if the project should continue and the source of the funding required for completion. If the project is affirmed and no capital (approved or contingency) remains, the council may fund the project as carry-forward capital in the subsequent years' calculation of net cash available or may require the project to be resubmitted for funding from the subsequent years' capital review process.

TYPE 3

Approved capital projects that have not been committed via purchase order or other written commitment in the year of approval will not be considered carry-forward capital, and they must be resubmitted to the capital management council for review in the subsequent allocation year.

Example 2

A 500-bed academic medical center (AMC) has calculated the capital constraint using the best-practice method described in this chapter. The AMC has adopted the carry-forward capital policies outlined in Example 1, with an exception associated with carry-forward capital for physician recruitment. Because of concern that strategically vital physician recruitment activities, anticipated for the current fiscal year, could be delayed or easily extend past the fiscal year without commitment, the AMC specifically excluded approved recruitment-related capital from Type 3 carry-forward capital. The AMC's executives essentially indicated that although intended for the current fiscal year, the capital associated with strategic recruitment would be handled as Type 1 carry-forward capital (i.e., a multiyear project). Thus, unless an extreme financial or strategic change occurred, this capital would automatically carry forward .

Table 3-1 provides, in matrix form, a summary of more generalized best-practice parameters related to carry-forward capital management and different

Table 3-1. Carry-Forward Capital Matrices

	Carry-Forward Type	Carry Forward Allowed?	Parameters
Threshold Capital	Type 1 (Planned multi-year expenditure)	Yes	• Periodic monitoring by capital management council • Ongoing revalidation of allocation as long as total project dollars remain at or below original project estimate • Revalidation of allocation and determination of incremental funding if project cost increase is within established variance parameters • Reassessment of project economics and validation of allocation decision if project cost increase is greater than established variance parameters
	Type 2 (Encumbered, but delayed, single-year expenditure)	Yes	• Revalidation of allocation as long as total project dollars remain at or below original project estimate • Reassessment of project economics and validation of allocation decision if project cost increase is greater than established variance parameters
	Type 3 (Unencumbered and delayed single-year expenditure)	No	• Resubmission to the capital management council as a new request
Nonthreshold Capital	Type 1 (Planned multiyear expenditure)	N/A	
	Type 2 (Encumbered, but delayed, single-year expenditure)	Yes	• Verification from operating entity management that expenditure level remains at or below budget • Limited carry-forward timing (e.g., 3 months)
	Type 3 (Unencumbered and delayed single-year expenditure)	No	

Source: Kaufman, Hall & Associates, Inc. Used with permission.

approaches applied to threshold capital and nonthreshold capital, as defined in Chapter Four.

Cash Reserve Requirements

The financial planning process identifies operating performance and balance sheet targets associated with meeting the capitalization needs of the organization while maintaining access to capital within defined credit and risk contexts. Liquidity—the minimum level of required cash reserves—is a key balance sheet target. As management projects operating performance, executives should also define the specific amount of generated cash flow that should be held on the organization's balance sheet. The increase or decrease in cash reserves is included in the capital constraint calculation. In this way, leaders can be certain that the amount of capital to be spent will not jeopardize the organization's balance sheet liquidity.

Conversely, if capital availability is calculated as a percentage of depreciation or income, there is no correlation to the balance sheet and no way to accurately understand the impact of a particular spending level on the organization's access to capital.

Other Sources and Uses of Cash

This catch-all category directs attention to the myriad of other nonincome statement calls on organizational cash that ultimately affect liquidity and cash available for capital spending. Among the more typical items are as follows:

- Funding of pension or benefit-related shortfalls
- Payouts to unaffiliated organizations, such as joint venture partners or corporate members
- Dividends received from unaffiliated organizations

These items can be either additions to or deductions from the capital constraint. Their inclusion and a proper accounting of their effects ensure that the ultimate capital constraint calculation reflects true levels of cash available for capital spending.

Putting It All Together

Table 3-2 illustrates a five-year capital constraint calculation performed by a two-hospital system based on its strategic financial plan. The sources and uses of capital numbers reflect the output of the financial plan and quantify the organization's strategic initiatives through volume, expense, and reimbursement projections that result in projected levels of net income, working capital, and cash reserves.

The system defined total cash available for spending in 2007 as approximately $31.1 million, but it subtracted from this a 10 percent capital contingency for systemwide emergency investments, yielding net cash available for allocation of nearly $28 million. Chapter Four addresses contingency capital in more detail.

Defending the Constraint

After calculating the capital constraint, management must be vigilant about ensuring that organizational spending does not exceed this sum and that capital investment does not occur outside of the organization's capital management process. High-level oversight must be provided by the capital management council. If the process breaks down and authorization of capital occurs outside of the comprehensive process, the validity of the capital constraint will be undermined and the integrity of the process diminished.

Leasing

In many organizations, leasing often challenges the capital constraint. Although operating leases frequently represent the most expensive source of capital for an organization, they are also used by some executives or managers to bypass the capital management process. This is especially true if the

Table 3-2. Calculating the Capital Constraint—Net Cash Available for Spending

		2007	2008	2009	2010	2011
	Operating Income	$ 17,587	$12,950	13,035	$14,104	$16,664
Add:	Nonoperating income (excluding interest)	6,364	9,864	7,989	8,064	11,039
	Depreciation and amortization	25,167	29,226	33,335	36,677	39,309
	Operating cash flow	49,118	52,040	54,359	58,845	67,012
Plus:	New debt proceeds (net of restriction)	—	43,096	—	—	—
	Nonincome statement philanthropy	—		—	—	—
	Interest income	4,885	4,583	4,820	5,431	6,177
	Total sources of cash available for capital	54,003	99,719	59,179	64,276	73,189
Less:	Working capital requirements	(1,012)	(1,083)	(1,748)	(1,999)	(2,195)
	Principal payments	(9,400)	(7,444)	(8,254)	(8,209)	(7,243)
	Other sources/(uses) of cash	—		—	—	—
	Carry-forward capital[1]	(23,104)	(12,949)	—	—	—
	Precommitted capital[1]	—		—	—	—
	Contributions to cash reserves	10,604	(9)	(15,710)	(20,882)	(30,251)
	Total uses of cash	(22,912)	(21,485)	(25,712)	(31,090)	(39,689)
	Total cash available for capital	31,091	78,234	33,467	33,186	33,500
	Less: 10% system capital contingency	(3,109)	(7,823)	(3,347)	(3,319)	(3,350)
	Net cash available for capital allocation	$ 27,982	$70,411	$30,120	$29,867	$30,150
	Total capital spending[2]	$ 54,195	$91,183	$33,467	$33,186	$33,500

Notes:

1. Transitional year only (fiscal year 2007).

2. Includes cash available for capital allocation, carry-forward capital, and precommitted capital

Source: Kaufman, Hall & Associates, Inc. Used with permission.

process does not include a clear definition of capital. For example, should the value of the lease for a medical office building, a leased outpatient facility, or a leased MRI be considered capital subject to the capital constraint?

Under the separation theorem of corporate finance, an organization's investment decisions must be independent both of the preferences of executives and of financing decisions. This means that organizations must separate evaluation of investment decisions from the financing of investment decisions. In the context of the capital management process, leasing is clearly a financing decision that, by definition, should be under the purview of the organization's corporate-level financial management, not a department manager or even a COO. Whether or not a particular capital request is considered within the capital constraint should be a function of the magnitude of the proposed investment rather than the structure (financing) under which it will be acquired.

What some managers present as leasing "opportunities," particularly the big opportunities, may represent end runs around the capital management process. For example, consider the organization that has established a capital constraint of $30 million and has allocated the full $30 million. However, two of the three requested CT scanners, totaling $5 million, did not make the cut. To appease the vocal department chair, or because an executive really wanted the CT scanners approved but was overruled by the council, the scanners are leased. Ostensibly, the leases create a zero footprint against the capital constraint. However, the use of leasing in this instance has simply rationalized capital spending beyond the capital constraint. Spending is now $35 million rather than the approved $30 million. In addition, because the capital constraint is a direct function of the organization's expected financial performance, the leasing-produced higher spending level will ultimately have negative financial consequences for organizational cash flow. Total uses of cash will be higher.

If the organization proceeds with the equipment leasing, its executives need to ask themselves the following questions:

- Why did we establish the $30 million capital constraint? (What purpose does it serve?)
- Given this infraction of the spending limit, what other capital-intensive projects might be approved outside of the established capital management process?

Moody's Investors Service, one of the three agencies that rate healthcare debt, released a "Special comment" providing its views on operating leases (Moody's Investors Service 2004). The agency indicated that it looks closely at an organization's use of operating leases to determine the effect of such financial obligations on the organization's debt capacity and credit quality. Although technically *off balance sheet*, Moody's considers operating leases and other "innovative financing" techniques to be *on credit*. This means that, in assessing debt capacity and credit quality, the agency incorporates leases as part of an organization's comprehensive debt program, "when material."

How much leasing can be implemented without negatively affecting the organization's financial health from a rating or creditor's perspective? To evaluate materiality, Moody's looks at the size of leasing "debt" relative to total debt outstanding. A red flag for materiality goes up when leases comprise more than about 15 percent of total debt (McIntire and Waldron 2006).

Information Technology

Allocation of capital for IT projects should be part of the organization-wide capital management process. Information technology capital should be handled like any other class of capital and should be evaluated within the best-practice capital management process. This ensures comprehensive consideration of the projects' short-term and long-term benefits and costs within the organization's overall portfolio of investments.

Potential IT investments, like all major potential investments, should benefit from the in-depth net present value and estimated net present value analyses described in Chapter Six. Analysis of IT capital should attempt to quantify, to the extent possible, all potential incremental operating costs and efficiencies over the life of the investment. These initiatives will likely have a lower net present value than other projects in the organization's portfolio because of their infrastructure-like nature. However, like other infrastructure investments that represent basic costs of doing business, IT investments should be viewed within a balanced portfolio that is supported by objective analytics. If executive and board leaders wish to proceed with the investment based on qualitative rather than quantitative reasons, they will be fully aware of the costs involved with the expenditure and the likely financial implications of the investment.

A clear definition of how much capital the organization can afford to spend is a prerequisite to defining capital pools, the subject of Chapter Four.

References

McIntire, M., and D. J. Waldron. 2006. "Funding Technology: Evaluating and Exercising the Leasing Option." *Healthcare Financial Management* 60 (11): 92–8, 100.

Moody's Investors Service. 2004. *Capital Access: Moody's View on Operating Leases: Off Balance Sheet But On Credit.* Special Comment. New York: Moody's Investors Service.

The Governance Institute. 2005. "New Rigor and Criteria: The Board's Role in Allocating Capital." *BoardRoom Press Newsletter* 16 (4): S1–S8.

Chapter Four

Defining the Capital Pools

The next step of best-practice capital management involves defining capital pools, which will enable more effective decision making and management. The goal of this step is to determine which dollars will be (and, by default, will not be) centrally managed and allocated to capital investment opportunities on the basis of in-depth, rigorous analysis. Not all capital requests may warrant the management time and attention required for detailed business planning and analysis. The structural definitions described in this chapter will identify those that do and will establish a means to manage the remaining capital requests.

This chapter does not advocate defining capital investment *buckets* (for example, ambulatory, inpatient, and routine capital) or capital investment *types* (for example, IT, medical equipment, and facility improvement capital) to which capital would be allocated separately. Quite the opposite, the following discussion is predicated on managing all capital in a consistent manner.

As described earlier and to be described more fully in Chapter Six, capital allocated for investment should reflect the organization's long-term strategic and financial vision. *All* major investments should be considered candidates for that capital within an overall portfolio of investment opportunities. Defining and segregating certain project or capital types preclude thorough examination of whether those categories are the right categories and whether each category warrants continued investment. Allocation of capital investment by buckets or types, in effect, disconnects the capital management process from the organization's current strategic direction.

Healthcare organizations with successful, best-practice capital management processes define three investment pools—an approach recommended for all organizations:

- A threshold capital pool
- A nonthreshold capital pool
- A contingency pool

The threshold and nonthreshold pools, described fully in the next section, should be the focus of allocation activity. The contingency pool, also described later in this chapter, supports and provides reserves for investment activity occurring through both the threshold and nonthreshold pools.

Why only two pools for *active* allocation? Why not three or four, or just one? Capital management is simply more efficient with fewer pools. Each pool has its associated logistical, monitoring, and informational requirements, so fewer are better. In addition, the use of only two pools minimizes the ability of organizational staff to access funds for capital outside of the established process. On the other hand, having one big pool creates an untenable management situation with onerous workloads associated with reviewing all capital requests. This situation is likely to result in a lower standard of review for every request.

The two-active-pool approach has proven to be most effective by many hospitals and health systems, generating positive results in terms of organizational acceptance, implementation, and financial performance. An organization's capital management council must clearly define the parameters for each pool and how capital in each pool can be accessed. A discussion of each follows.

The Threshold and Nonthreshold Capital Concept

At present in the healthcare industry, pool designations vary widely from organization to organization. Some hospitals and health systems use "strategic capital" and "routine capital" as pool descriptors; others use "growth capital" and "replacement capital"; still others use a myriad of different terms. Each categorization typically has unique attributes based on its historical development and organizational culture.

Descriptors can be confusing. What makes some capital requests strategic and others routine? Is capital used for a replacement hospital considered replacement capital or growth capital?

Without precise and consistent definitions, there is often uncertainty within the organization about which funds can and should be accessed. Beyond the organization in the capital markets, which rate and insure the debt used to finance initiatives, there may also be uncertainty about appropriateness of capital spending levels and initiatives.

Beyond definitions, the manner in which organizations manage the pools also varies widely. Should requests in separate pools in fact be evaluated differently? For example, should requests for replacement capital be exempt from analyses because everyone knows that replacement capital does not generate a return? How far should that freedom extend?

Although analyses may not be needed for replacement of a hospital bed or an x-ray room, what about for replacement of all facility beds in a large hospital system (which can run into the tens of millions of dollars) and for more complex and costly replacements? For example, what kind of analysis is appropriate for a replacement hospital or the multimillion-dollar replacement of imaging technology, such as an MRI? Are these strategic investments that require in-depth analytics or simply routine replacement investments? Again, without precise and consistent definitions, confusion often arises.

Best-practice corporate finance suggests that all major capital requests, as defined by the organization, should benefit from analytical rigor. Kaufman, Hall & Associates, Inc., have thus introduced to healthcare the concept of threshold capital. *Threshold* is defined as a point of entering or beginning or the quantitative point at which an action is triggered. The *capital threshold* is defined as a specific dollar amount. *Threshold capital* is any proposed capital expenditure above the defined capital threshold. All threshold capital will require comprehensive analysis and centralized review. The dollar amount, in effect, triggers analysis and review.

Setting the threshold for any particular organization is both an art and a science, but it should result in a definite number. The science involves analysis of historical capital spending to determine the project dollar level at which the majority—anywhere from 65 percent to 80 percent—of an organization's capital initiatives will be required to undergo consistent, transparent, and rigorous quantitative analytics. The art is in evaluating how many project proposals are likely to be generated at a particular dollar threshold and assessing the organization's ability to appropriately prepare and review the required analyses.

If the organization employs a manual analytical process, the number of manageable projects may be small. On the other hand, if the organization uses one of the available capital management software tools, the number of projects that can be analyzed and reviewed by the organization may be 40 or more. Organizations that are able to prepare, review, and manage extensive project analyses can consider setting a lower threshold-capital dollar level, which better ensures data-driven and high-quality decision making.

Across the healthcare industry, threshold capital ranges from $25,000 at some small community hospitals to $5 million at the corporate level of large multistate health systems. Whatever the threshold dollar amount for an organization, the number should be hard and fast—in other words, applied organization-wide without exceptions. The capital threshold should also be reviewed periodically for continuing appropriateness, typically as a standard part of the annual capital management process.

Application of the capital threshold is very simple. Any project with an associated cost that is equal to or greater than the defined threshold dollar amount is considered threshold capital. Such projects should be funded from the threshold capital pool based on direct comparison to other proposed capital initiatives, as described in Chapter Six. The approach relies on rigorous, standardized quantitative and qualitative analysis. Nonthreshold capital, defined as requests with associated costs below the threshold dollar amount, are handled in a decentralized fashion, as described in Chapter Five.

Funding the Pools

Best-practice capital management requires organizations to define the principles under which total cash available for capital spending will be allocated among the capital pools.

Allocation to the contingency pool is straightforward and typically reflects a percentage of the total cash available for spending. Review of capital management practices in health systems nationwide indicates that health systems corporate contingency pools vary between 5 percent and 15 percent, with the vast majority of systems allocating 10 percent of total cash flow to the contingency pool (Sussman 2005). As described in Chapter Three, the remainder of available funds is the organization's capital constraint.

Funding levels for the threshold and nonthreshold capital pools are much more variable nationwide. However, the goal of a best-practice capital management process is to ensure analytic rigor and discipline with the vast majority of the organization's capital spending—65 percent to 80 percent.

Figure 4-1 illustrates how the two-hospital system described in Chapter Three, with a capital constraint calculation illustrated in Table 3-2, apportions capital to the threshold and nonthreshold pools. The system's *total* capital available for spending is $31.1 million. It allocates 10 percent of this or $3.1 million to the contingency pool, leaving $28 million as its net capital available for spending or its capital constraint. The system allocates 50 percent of this sum to the threshold capital pool and 50 percent to the nonthreshold capital pool.

Many organizations apportion the defined capital constraint so as to have approximately 75 percent of capital to be spent as threshold capital under the purview of the capital management council. Because the 75 percent includes carry-forward capital, the actual percentage division of the current-year capital constraint between the threshold and nonthreshold pools may actually be 50/50; Table 4-1 illustrates the mathematics of such a situation.

This health system's council will need to evaluate the percentage allocations on an annual basis to account for changes in the amount of carry-forward capital. The council should maintain the objective of achieving oversight of 75 percent of total capital spending. Any changes to the annual pool allocations will clearly be made within the agreed-upon allocation structure. To do otherwise would create an unnecessary level of organizational uncertainty, increase potential politicization of the allocation process, diminish the transparency of the process, and undermine its integrity.

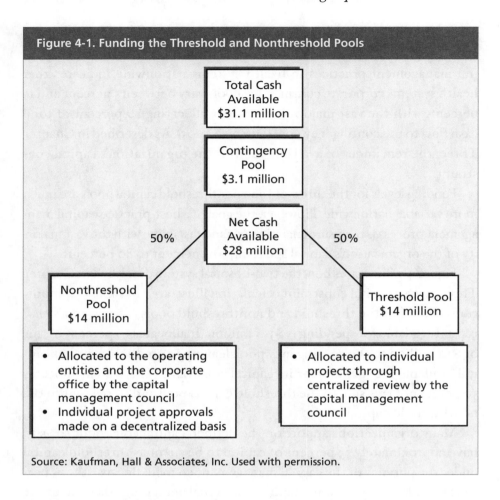

Figure 4-1. Funding the Threshold and Nonthreshold Pools

Source: Kaufman, Hall & Associates, Inc. Used with permission.

Managing and Using the Capital Investment Pools

The council or committee established to govern the allocation and application of funds available in each of the three capital investment pools—threshold capital, nonthreshold capital, and contingency—should be defined by documented policy on the basis of management position.

Threshold Capital

The threshold capital pool is the bolus of dollars allocated to fund threshold capital requests, defined as capital projects with costs in excess of the

Table 4-1. Calculation of Total Allocation of Cash Available to Capital Pools

Net cash available for capital	$28,000
Add: Contingency	3,100
Carry-forward capital	23,100
Precommitted capital	—
Total allocated capital	**$54,200**
Net cash available allocated to	
Threshold capital at 50%	$14,000
Carry-forward capital	23,100
Precommitted capital	—
50% of contingency capital	1,550
Total threshold capital	**$38,650**
Threshold capital as a % of total capital	**71.3%**

Source: Kaufman, Hall & Associates, Inc. Used with permission.

preestablished dollar amount. Threshold capital projects are often strategic, if only based on the fact that they have large dollar costs and are most often derived from the organization's strategic financial plan.

The threshold capital pool should be managed centrally, under the aegis of a council that has appropriate representation of key organizational constituencies. The council should govern all aspects of the threshold capital process to ensure the broadest possible context for decision making. Chapter Six provides a more detailed look at the evaluation of threshold capital initiatives.

Nonthreshold Capital

Management of the nonthreshold capital pool should be decentralized and be under the aegis of local managers. In a small, stand-alone hospital, decisions regarding nonthreshold capital might be made at the vice president level. In a large, academic medical center, delegation may be based on scope of authority (for example, clinical versus administrative) at a more senior level. A mini-allocation process might then occur under the guidance of the senior-level manager. In a multihospital environment, nonthreshold capital management typically occurs at the entity or regional level, where focus on market-specific needs can be addressed.

Independent of organization size and structure, the analytic requirements associated with nonthreshold capital should be far fewer than those for threshold capital. The majority of these expenditures will be more ongoing in nature, such as those addressing many low-dollar infrastructure and asset replacement needs.

Because the nonthreshold capital pool represents a small part of the organization's total capital spending and because typically there are a large volume of small dollar requests, information associated with the requests should be focused on categories of need, cost, and source. This type of information is vital to the efficiency of group purchasing decisions and the management of cash flow timing.

Contingency Capital

The contingency pool, which comes off the top of the total cash flow available for capital spending, is intended to support threshold capital needs. Therefore, it should be managed by the council as a safety valve to address the following:

- Funding of unanticipated emergencies, such as capital required to address unforeseen facility code violations or equipment failure that will materially affect a core business or the quality of patient care
- Supplementing capital availability when operating performance does not reach levels assumed in calculating the capital constraint
- Funding of real off-cycle requests related to opportunities that were truly unknown at the time of the batch allocation process (note: such requests should occur infrequently)

The contingency pool should not be used to supplement the nonthreshold pool, which is managed on a decentralized basis. The council should also determine how to handle unused contingency dollars. Should such dollars go back into the equation for the following year's available dollars, or should they be added to current-year capital spending?

The answer to this question will vary by organization and by year. Nonetheless, the council should be vested with the authority to determine the application of unused contingency dollars. This ensures a broader, more strategic discussion leading to an enhanced decision. Often, contingency capital is divided for use among threshold projects and the allocated nonthreshold pool using the same distribution methods as were employed initially. For example, if an organization initially allocated 75 percent of capital to the threshold pool and 25 percent to the nonthreshold pool, released unused contingency funds would be apportioned the same way.

Following the apportioning of available capital into threshold capital, nonthreshold capital, and contingency pools, the organization's capital management council can consider how to further allocate and evaluate nonthreshold capital, the subject of Chapter Five.

Reference

Sussman, J. H. 2005. *Survey of Capital Allocation Approaches in 26 U.S. Health Systems.* Skokie, IL: Kaufman, Hall & Associates, Inc.

CHAPTER FIVE

Allocating and Evaluating Nonthreshold Capital

CAPITAL MANAGEMENT COUNCILS in all healthcare organizations must determine the proportion of the capital constraint to be allocated to fund nonthreshold capital requests. The management of nonthreshold capital is typically decentralized, as described in Chapter Four.

This chapter describes the method and approach used by the council to determine how nonthreshold capital will be allocated among the operating units competing for that capital. Depending on the organization, this might include departments, service lines, regions, hospitals, or other organizational entities. The organizational challenge is to allocate nonthreshold dollars in a way that will meet minimum capital needs and reward performance at the operating-unit level.

Every operating unit has ongoing capital needs for equipment and other replacement capital, such as personal computers or patient monitors, and for infrastructure investment, such as lobby renovations or utility upgrades. Clearly, these requirements must be met in order for the unit to remain functional and in operation. Meeting these requirements is a basic cost of doing business.

Basic cost notwithstanding, the method used to allocate nonthreshold capital should make it clear that the dollars are not an annual right or a gift that automatically will be given year in and year out. The method used to allocate nonthreshold dollars should create incentives for each operating unit to be as successful as possible to maximize the dollars received.

Allocation Principles

The method used by an organization to allocate nonthreshold capital to its operating units should address the following questions:

- How can and should the allocation of nonthreshold capital be linked to quantifiable, long-term measures of success? What measures should be used?
- Within this context, how can appropriate levels of nonthreshold capital be allocated to nonprofitable, nonrevenue-producing, or small operating units?
- How can gaming of the allocation and management process be prevented or, at least, minimized?

Sidebar 5-1 provides principles related to allocating nonthreshold capital used by one organization, which can be adopted or adapted by other organizations.

The issue covered by the first question can generally be addressed with ease in multiunit health systems, which typically have well-defined operating unit structures and ongoing measurement of unit-based performance. The current best-practice method used by health systems nationwide is based on measurement of relative operating EBITDA, defined as operating earnings before interest, taxes, depreciation, and amortization expenses.

Operating EBITDA provides a highly comparable measure of pure operating profitability—a measure that is not affected by past capital-related decisions made by the unit or by the corporate office. For example, consider a unit that has underinvested in capital (i.e., not spent what it needs to spend to ensure market and financial performance outlined in the strategic financial plan). Because the unit will have lower depreciation expense than a unit that funds its capital needs, it will also have a higher operating margin. If nonthreshold capital were allocated on the basis of operating margin, this unit would receive more capital than a similar unit that has been diligent about maintaining appropriate levels of capital investment. Should the underinvesting unit be rewarded for its lack-of-capital-spending behavior? By focusing the allocation of nonthreshold capital on EBITDA, however, the units are compared on the basis of true, year-to-year profitability.

Sidebar 5-1. Principles for Allocating Nonthreshold Capital

- Allocation of nonthreshold capital initially will be driven formulaically on the basis of each operating unit's performance relative to the organization's overall performance.
- All formula-based allocations may be adjusted by the council to ensure that all operating units receive appropriate minimum capital levels.
- All *patient operating units*, defined as those entities with patient revenue, will receive a minimum allocation of nonthreshold capital, as defined by the council.
- *Nonpatient operating units* will receive a minimum allocation of nonthreshold capital as determined by the council, or will they have their nonthreshold capital requests funded by patient operating units with which they are directly associated (for example, a segregated laundry corporation).
- The council will reconsider the nonthreshold capital minimum annually and make adjustments as appropriate.

Source: Kaufman, Hall & Associates, Inc. Used with permission.

Applying the relative EBITDA methodology, the council can evaluate historical operating performance of individual units and calculate the relative contribution of each unit to overall organizational profitability. This is best defined as a percentage of total operating EBITDA over a defined period of time, typically at least 24 months. A shorter-than-24-month period places the operating units at significant capital allocation risk based on the impact of a bad year and creates a highly volatile allocation environment. A longer period of at least 24 months smoothes out such variability and rewards or withholds reward only on the basis of sustained trends.

This relative performance approach can also be used by stand-alone hospitals or other organizations that are not part of a multiunit structure. Every organization has or should have internal performance measures that management employs to monitor success. Furthermore, most organizations have hierarchical management structures with delegated operating authority.

An example would be a community hospital with a first-level management structure, which includes the CEO, COO, CFO, and other chief executives, and a second level of management at the vice-president level, which manages different aspects of hospital operations. The management structure includes a vice president for nursing, for clinical services (ancillary departments), for support services, and for facilities. How should the community hospital's council allocate nonthreshold capital to each of these vice presidents in an objective and consistent manner?

Three facts should be kept in mind by the council of this community hospital:

- The proportion of dollars allocated to nonthreshold capital in this hospital is approximately 25 percent of the organization's total capital.
- Allocated nonthreshold dollars typically are to be spent on low-dollar expenditures that have little to no expected financial return.
- It is difficult if not impossible to accurately calculate EBITDA associated with each vice president's area of responsibility, especially for an executive such as the vice president of facilities, who has no revenue-generating departments within his or her purview.

As a result, the council should define other measures of performance to use as the basis for allocating available nonthreshold dollars to vice presidents' areas of responsibility. Measures of performance will vary by organization; no one measure or combination of measures is right. Several commonly applied measures include the following:

- Contribution to historical organization-wide operating and capital budget variances (low variances would be rewarded with more capital)
- Number of full-time equivalents (FTEs), which would correlate people with capital (units with more people would receive more capital)
- Relative percentage of operating costs (units with higher costs would receive more capital)

The first method, which links low budget variances to higher capital, directly rewards vice presidents for appropriate cost management. The second approach, which links the number of staff with allocated capital, reflects the realities of hospital operations but could contribute to escalating costs resulting from "FTE creep." The third approach, which rewards departments with higher expenditures by giving them capital, may be neither desirable nor appropriate in a payment-constrained, cost-escalating environment. Again, none of these methods is perfect, but an organization's council should give serious thought to the most appropriate measure or measures of department-specific performance.

Allocation to Nonrevenue-Producing, Nonprofitable, or Small Operating Units

How should nonthreshold capital be allocated to operating units that, because of their size, function, or historical financial performance, would receive an inadequate allocation of nonthreshold capital through a formula-based process?

Every health system or hospital has some operating units or collection of units that fit this description. Each entity—whether a corporate office, a laundry service, or a number of purely administrative departments—has capital requirements. The organization must have a reasonable mechanism by which nonthreshold capital can be allocated to such entities.

Organizations use different approaches. One of the most prevalent methods nationwide is to define a minimum dollar-amount allocation for such operating units. The challenge is to establish a minimum allocation in a manner that minimizes politics and maximizes objectivity. Organizations that have successfully tackled this challenge most frequently have a broad-based governance structure, as described in Chapter Two. Through vesting this type of decision making in a council rather than in the CEO or some other individual, a negotiated but objective minimum allocation of capital typically can be made.

Small Health System Example

The council of a two-hospital health system allocated 70 percent of capital to the threshold capital pool and 30 percent to the nonthreshold capital pool. The council determined that the hospital that contributed a bit more than 78 percent of the system's profitability during the past 24 months would

Table 5-1. Allocating Nonthreshold Capital in a Two-Hospital Health System

	Profitability ($000s)	% of Total Profitability	Allocated Nonthreshold Capital	Actual Percent Allocation
Hospital A	$ 83,834	78.1%	$11,207	77.8%
Hospital B	23,540	21.9	3,143	21.8
Corporate	0	0.0	50	0.4
Total system	$107,374	100.0%	$14,400	100.0%

Source: Kaufman, Hall & Associates, Inc. Used with permission.

receive a bit less than 78 percent of the system's nonthreshold capital allocation of 30 percent. Table 5-1 notes that the council allocated $50,000 to the corporate office in spite of the fact that the corporate office did not generate a positive EBITDA. The council established this minimum allocation in recognition of corporate office needs for replacement of minor equipment. The council made the $50,000 allocation by proportionately reducing each of the two hospitals' allocations, effectively reducing Hospital A's allocation from 78.1 percent to 77.8 percent of nonthreshold capital.

Large Health System Example

The council of an 11-hospital health system used EBITDA as the measure of profitability on which to base nonthreshold capital allocation. However, recognizing the insufficiency of the formula-based allocation for various system entities, the council also established minimum nonthreshold capital levels for each of the units. As indicated in Table 5-2, certain minima were based on contractual obligations (e.g., Hospital G), while others recognized that every unit needed some capital (e.g., the central business office and the laundry).

The council established still other minimum levels based on its analysis of an entity's past spending habits and anticipated future needs. Based on the established minimum allocations, the council adjusted allocation percentages to each of the operating units and defined specific dollar allocations.

Table 5-2. Allocating Nonthreshold Capital in a Large Health System

Adjusted EBITDA	Adjusted EBITDA	Allocable EBITDA	% of Total EBITDA	Allocation of $13,608	Allocation Adjustments to Minimum	Allocation of $13,608	Final Allocation Percentage
Hospital A	$38,373	$ 38,373	38.3%	$ 5,206	$ —	$ 4,394	32.3%
Hospital B	29,839	29,839	29.8	4,049	—	3,417	25.1
Hospital C	13,530	13,530	13.5	1,836	—	1,549	11.4
Hospital D	5,060	5,060	5.0	687	—	579	4.3
Hospital E	340	340	0.3	46	125	125	0.9
Hospital F	905	905	0.9	123	125	125	0.9
Hospital G	3,118	3,118	3.1	423	750	750	5.5
Hospital H	845	845	0.8	115	370	370	2.7
Hospital I	—	—	0.0	—	—	—	0.0
Hospital J	8,286	8,286	8.3	1,124	—	949	7.0
Hospital K	—	—	0.0	—	—	—	0.0
Central Business Office	(45,549)	—	0.0	—	100	100	0.7
Laundry	—	—	0.0	—	100	100	0.7
Information Systems	—	—	0.0	—	750	750	5.5
Corporate Services	(45,549)	—	0.0	—	400	400	2.9
Education	—	—	0.0	—	—	—	0.0
Health Centers	—	—	0.0	—	—	—	0.0
Total ABC Health System	$ 9,198	$100,296	100.0%	$13,608	$2,720	$13,608	100.0%

Source: Kaufman, Hall & Associates, Inc. Used with permission.

Evaluating Nonthreshold Capital Projects

The evaluation and approval of nonthreshold capital requests should also be as consistent as possible within the context of its decentralized management. By definition, nonthreshold capital requests are smaller in dollar amount. Typically, these requests are also more limited in their organizational impact. As a result, the analytic requirements for nonthreshold capital requests do not need to be as *comprehensive* as those for threshold capital requests. But they should be just as *rigorous*.

Because of the sheer volume of nonthreshold capital requests, organizations, in fact, should establish a rigid structure to elicit required information and an appropriate review process. Although the organization's council *does not* need to review and approve specific requests, evaluation by the appropriate departmental or organizational body is vital.

As mentioned earlier, decisions related to nonthreshold capital investment should be made by local operating unit executives, whether a vice president within a stand-alone hospital or the CEO or management group of a hospital in a multihospital system. Regardless, certain organization-level evaluation should be performed. For example, organizations benefit when all IT requests undergo a *functional review* by a centralized information systems team that focuses on the following criteria:

• Relevance of the request
• Consistency of the request with organizational standards and requirements
• Appropriateness of estimated costs and timing
• Opportunities for combining the request with other similar requests to gain purchasing efficiency and power

Similar functional-review committees could be established for capital requests related to clinical equipment and facility improvement. Through such reviews, operating unit management and the organization as a whole can achieve a consistent approach to specific types of capital investment.

The use of standardized capital request forms ensures the collection of required general information (for example, item description, number of units, vendor, cost). It also enables the organization to define and obtain information related to the operating or financial benefits that might accrue to the organization as a result of the investment. Figure 5-1 provides a sample request form for nonthreshold capital.

The organization's council can also establish specific nonquantitative criteria to be used in the evaluation of nonthreshold capital requests. Additional evaluation enhances informed decision making. Inclusion of information about financial impact also enables management to measure, through budget variance analysis, the ultimate success of the purchase or investment.

Figure 5-1. Request Form for Nonthreshold Capital

Radiology–Nuclear Medicine
Request Number: 2007_27220_01

Requested Name	Surgical gamma probe
Requested Description	Surgical gamma probe
Project Group	Proposed Vendor
Justification	An additional nuclear medicine gamma probe is needed for multiple exams

Class	2–Replacement	Reason	6–Strategic plan
Category	Medical equipment	Priority	2–Medium
Subcategory	Radiology	Purchase Period	2–April-June

Capital Cost Summary

Unit Cost	$34,000
# Items	1
Subtotal	$34,000
Sales Tax:	$0
Shipping/handling	$0
Additional capital (below)	$0
Other	$0
Less trade in	$0
Total capital request	$34,000

Decision Matrix

Impact on patient and/or physician satisfaction	Quality, safety, and compliance effectiveness	Strategic and new business growth	Impact on employee work experience	Financial performance
2–Modest positive impact for either	2–Modest impact	2–Has potential for growth	1–No impact on employee satisfaction	2–Bottom line positive impact >$25,000

Optional functional review requests

2–Clinical/BioMed	4–Purchasing	No review	No review

Source: Kaufman, Hall & Associates, Inc. Used with permission.

Because nonthreshold capital review is by design decentralized, the ultimate approach to the evaluation of these capital requests, as implemented by operating unit executives, will uniquely reflect the unit's culture and structure. However unique the process, its effectiveness will be directly tied to its objectivity and consistency. Furthermore, through transparent communication of nonthreshold capital decisions and the underlying reasoning, top management has an opportunity to educate managers organization-wide and continually improve the quality of nonthreshold capital requests and decision making.

The next chapter addresses the topic of evaluating threshold capital investment opportunities.

CHAPTER SIX

Evaluating Threshold Capital Investment Opportunities

IMAGINE TRYING TO play baseball without any rules. Three strikes do not make an out, so the neighborhood bully remains at the plate, swinging away for hours. When he tires, whoever races to the plate first gets to hit next. Teams do not have a set number of players on the field, so Team A has 18 people positioned between center field and right field, and Team B has only one player covering the whole outfield. Who will win this game? In fact, is this a game worth playing? Without a level playing field, wouldn't and shouldn't one team quit in disgust?

One-Batch Review

Capital allocation is not a game, but fairness in hospital and health system executive suites is just as important as it is on ball fields. Equal opportunity for every initiative under consideration is ensured through an organization's insistence on a formal, one-batch review process that uses uniform, consistent evaluative criteria, thereby facilitating direct comparison of competing capital initiatives.

In a best-practice, one-batch review process, all projects—whether likely to generate a positive return on investment (ROI) or not—are reviewed and capital is allocated once a year as a complete portfolio. Each and every investment opportunity—whether for a new ambulatory clinic, high-end scanner, quality initiative, decision support system, or another IT system—should be considered within the entire portfolio of potential investments, as described later in the chapter.

Analyses of projects that have a negative ROI are as, if not more, important as analyses of projects with a positive ROI. The overall process does not rule out profitless capital requests. If the capital management council wishes to proceed with a profitless investment based on qualitative or other reasons besides quantitative value, at least the organization will be fully aware of the costs involved and the likely outcomes of the expenditure (Kaufman 2003).

Because it supports a portfolio perspective of capital allocation, the one-batch review approach eases process management and provides complete control over the amount and type of capital expenditures. The result is an enhanced ability to ensure alignment between proposed capital investments and strategic goals. For the one-batch approach to be successful, however, the organization must be able to view proposed capital expenditures within the organization's overall strategic context. In addition, decisions to allocate capital must occur in a time frame that enables the organization to incorporate approved projects into the current-year operating and capital budgets.

For organizations that have established an integrated process calendar, like the one described earlier, one-batch allocation is easily accomplished. It can and has been done successfully at healthcare organizations of all sizes, structures, and operating orientations, whether for-profit, not-for-profit, faith-based, or community-based.

One of the objections often raised about the use of one-batch allocation of capital is the perceived inability of project sponsors to complete the required analysis within established time frames. Comments most often heard include, "We don't learn of these investment opportunities until the last minute, when there's no time to complete an analysis," or "There are too many projects and not enough time."

Actual experience in organizations with a coherent, well-designed capital management process, however, belies the validity of these objections. Because the process of allocating capital is an annual one, it is similar to the existing, cyclical capital process at most organizations. Previously unforeseen, last-minute opportunities are, in reality, few and far between. When they do arise, however, the capital management process must provide a mechanism for their review, as described in Chapter Seven, while maintaining total spending within the capital constraint. Senior managers should rarely be caught unaware of projects requiring significant dollar investments. A corporate finance–based capital management process simply forces the project champion to be more rigorous in planning to ensure that the analysis is ready for submission at the appropriate time.

Standardized Formats or Templates

To facilitate informed decision making, each threshold capital investment opportunity should benefit from development of a thorough business plan. The plan describes the business concept and its financial effect in significant detail, thereby providing the basic documentation and analysis necessary for a valid capital decision.

All threshold capital project analyses should be submitted using a single, standardized planning template that provides a uniform analytical approach. This will help ensure true comparability. It also enables executives and managers organization-wide to adopt a shared vision of the key drivers of financial success (Malehorn 2005).

Required Information

Whether called a business plan or a threshold capital project review form, the critical components should include the following:

- Description of the proposed capital initiative, including
  - o Consistency with and enhancement of the organization's mission and core values
  - o Alignment to the organization's strategic plan and initiatives
- Quantification of the capital investment required to initiate and complete the proposed project
- Projection of the initial and ongoing operating requirements associated with the proposed project

- Utilization projections and related assumptions
- Delineation of the potential market to be served and the means by which that market will be attracted
- Detailed quantitative analysis to identify potential ROI and key financial risks associated with the investment, including
    o   Projected financial impact (five or ten years)
    o   Projected cash flow
    o   Net present value and expected net present value (risk adjusted)
    o   Feasibility study for fundraising, as appropriate
- Qualitative factors, such as effect on
    o   Organization's mission and strategies
    o   Organization's competitive position in the market
    o   Critical groups of stakeholders
    o   Quality of patient care
- Identification of potential exit strategies and related performance measures

This business planning information integrates data from numerous sources, including strategic plan outputs, operating estimates, and capital estimates, to generate a complete, risk-adjusted view of an initiative's ROI (see Figure 6-1). Key areas of business risk relate to achievement of projected volume levels, control of project costs, achievement of anticipated operating efficiencies, and management of productivity. Risk analysis, as described later, focuses on the relative importance, the probability of occurrence, and the impact of risk on a project's potential financial return.

Financial projections are a standard requirement in all business planning. To maintain validity throughout the organization, the projection development process itself should be supported by a standardized tool that

- defines a structured projection format;
- incorporates globally applicable assumptions established at an organizational level;
- requires specific delineation of all key assumptions;
- includes all quantitative and qualitative review criteria; and
- uses corporate finance–based techniques, such as weighted average cost of capital, discounted cash flow, and net present value.

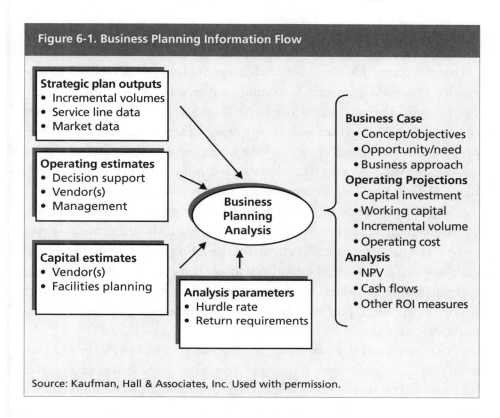

Figure 6-1. Business Planning Information Flow

Strategic plan outputs
- Incremental volumes
- Service line data
- Market data

Operating estimates
- Decision support
- Vendor(s)
- Management

Capital estimates
- Vendor(s)
- Facilities planning

Business Planning Analysis

Analysis parameters
- Hurdle rate
- Return requirements

Business Case
- Concept/objectives
- Opportunity/need
- Business approach

Operating Projections
- Capital investment
- Working capital
- Incremental volume
- Operating cost

Analysis
- NPV
- Cash flows
- Other ROI measures

Source: Kaufman, Hall & Associates, Inc. Used with permission.

By definition, the *quantitative* components of business planning for threshold capital opportunities focus on margin; the *qualitative* components focus on mission. Creating a balance between margin and mission is accomplished through weighting quantitative and qualitative factors during the decision-making process. This concept will be described later in the chapter.

Quantitative Analysis Using Corporate Finance–Based Techniques

Quantitative analysis using corporate finance–based techniques provides the fact base for informed decision making about capital investment opportunities. With involvement of key stakeholders, organizations should establish standardized criteria for the evaluation and selection of such opportunities and involve key team members in the process of ranking and scoring capital requests.

Most organizations include financial return as one of the significant project decision-making criteria, but seldom is it relied on as the only criterion. Furthermore, the weight associated with financial return as a criterion varies by organization. Organizations clearly cannot carry a series of investment decisions that do not add value to the organization. Best-practice capital management allows management discretion, but it uses quantitative, rigorous analytics to provide a transparent, financial context for all decisions.

Effective allocation of capital depends on the competent use of quantitative techniques used in corporate finance. These include the calculation of net cash available for capital, incremental cash flow projections, discounted cash flows, and net present value. In addition, consideration of risk, through techniques such as Monte Carlo simulation, should be a standard component of the evaluation of potential cash flows. The mechanics of selected techniques are described later in the chapter.

A consensus-driven approach to allocating capital—one focused on what may "feel good" and "look nice"—does not provide the quantitative measures necessary to evaluate financial return. The use of rigorous quantitative techniques ensures a common language and outcomes or end points that can be compared for each project under consideration. When push comes to shove, an organization's long-term viability and value stem from its ability to generate a financial return. Each project's return needs to be quantified. A portfolio-based positive return gives the organization the ability to invest in the next portfolio of strategies.

Return-on-Investment Methodologies

Standard measures for quantifying ROI include net present value (NPV), internal rate of return (IRR), payback period, annual return on capital (ROC), and annual return on equity (ROE). Sidebar 6-1 provides brief definitions.

Net present value, a core analytical approach used in corporate finance, distills the financial ebbs and flows of a project to a single dollar value. Internal rate of return calculates the interest rate needed to generate an NPV of zero. Although these approaches mirror one another, there are

Sidebar 6-1. Return-on-Investment Methodologies

Net present value (NPV)
A project's net contribution to financial performance—the value of future cash flows in today's dollars minus the required initial investment

Internal rate of return (IRR)
The rate of interest that discounts future net inflows from the proposed investment down to the amount invested (i.e., the rate of discount that makes NPV = 0)

Payback period
The length of time required for cash generated from an investment to equal the amount of cash originally invested in the project

Annual return on invested capital (ROC)
The annual net income generated by a project investment as a percentage of the original total project investment

Annual return on equity (ROE)
The annual net income generated by a project investment as a percentage of the original equity invested in the project

Sources: Adapted from Brealey, R. A., and S. C. Myers. 2000. *Principles of Corporate Finance*, 6th ed. New York: McGraw-Hill; Baker, J. W., and R. W. Baker. 2000. *Health Care Finance: Basic Tools for Nonfinancial Managers*. Gaithersburg, MD: Aspen Publications.

some significant differences. Internal rate of return assumes that all cash flows generated will be reinvested at the same rate (i.e., the IRR), which may not be the case in reality. In other words, cash flows generated by a project with an IRR of 15 percent are assumed to earn 15 percent. This may be an overly optimistic assumption. Additionally, it is difficult if not impossible to use IRR to evaluate a project that has no up-front capital investment.

For example, consider an initiative to develop a new service or program. The required initial investment would be limited to new staff and operating supplies for the first six to nine months of operations. None of the investment costs would be depreciable but rather would be incremental operating costs associated with the new service. Without a definable capital cost, IRR analysis fails. In contrast, such a project would be easily evaluated using NPV, which tracks cash inflows and cash outflows, distinguishing cash flows only by their timing and not by their underlying nature.

Payback period looks at the sequence of cash flows out and in to determine the point at which they equal each other. Return on capital evaluates the annual net income generated by a project relative to the total amount of capital invested in the project. If an organization invests $1 million in a piece of equipment that generates annual net income of $200,000, the annual ROC is 20 percent. Annual ROE evaluates the annual net income generated by a project relative to the total amount of original equity invested in the project. For example, if the same $1 million equipment purchase is financed by an $800,000 capital lease, the equity investment is only $200,000. If the equipment generates net income of $200,000, the annual ROE is 100 percent. Annual ROE is commonly used to evaluate real-estate development and leasing investments. Another term used for ROE is cash-on-cash return.

Each of these methods can contribute positively to comprehensive project analysis, but the ability of each to account for important factors, such as the following, varies widely (see Table 6-1):

- *Noncapital investment:* cash investment needed to initiate a project; used for purposes other than land, facilities, or equipment
- *The time value of money:* a dollar today is worth more than a dollar in the future
- *Project return over its lifetime:* the timing and magnitude of cash flows generated by investments vary by project
- *Inclusion of financing assumptions:* whether the investment is financed through debt, leasing, or some other financing mechanism

All of the methods, with the exception of IRR, take into account non-capital investment. Only NPV and IRR account for the time value of money, thereby working backward over the life of a project to evaluate the value (and opportunity costs) in today's dollars.

Net present value, IRR, and payback period evaluate ROI over the life of the project. Return on capital and ROE are annual measures and, as such,

Table 6-1. Comparison of ROI Methodologies

Method	Accounts for Noncapital Investment?	Accounts for Time Value of Money?	Accounts for Project Life Return?	Includes Financing Assumption?
NPV	Yes	Yes	Yes	No
IRR	No	Yes	Yes	No
Payback period	Yes	No	Yes	Yes
ROC	Yes	No	No	Yes
ROE	Yes	No	No	Yes

Source: Kaufman, Hall & Associates, Inc. Used with permission.

do not take into account an investment's return over the project life or the time value of money. Payback period, ROC, and ROE each includes interest cost in net income calculations.

Financing assumptions, such as interest cost in a "lease versus buy" decision, should be separated from the actual investment analysis. Only NPV and IRR properly separate investment and financing decision making. *Investment decisions* should focus on the appropriateness and potential value of the project; *financing decisions* for selected projects should be made on a portfolio basis at the corporate treasury level.

Concurrent use of all five methodologies often provides a very complete picture of a project's ROI, but even the most sophisticated of organizations are unlikely to do this because of the time and effort involved. In reality, NPV and IRR are the methods of choice for project analysis in many healthcare organizations. These organizations identify a hurdle rate, defined as the rate of return required—that the portfolio of investment opportunities should generate to meet the cash flow requirements of the organization's long-term capital plan.

Organizations also frequently calculate payback period for projects with a positive NPV. This defines how long it will take to recover invested cash and at what stage in the project's life the NPV is really being generated. If a project with a positive NPV has a long payback period, the organization knows it will be relying on longer-term cash flows to generate the positive return.

Expected net present value (ENPV) analysis, which adds risk analysis to NPV analysis, is the most valuable technique used to analyze a potential investment. Because ENPV analysis builds on NPV analysis, it is important to thoroughly describe the components of NPV analysis before applying risk assessment approaches.

Net-Present-Value Analysis

As mentioned earlier, this straightforward and reliable technique distills the financial ebbs and flows of a project to a single dollar value. Because it does so, it enables a project to be evaluated on its own merits and helps answer the question of how the project might compare financially to others under consideration. Generally, each project requires some initial investment. This is followed by a start-up period during which financial (i.e., cash flow) losses may occur. Then, hopefully, project net cash flows approach zero and, ultimately, enter a period of financial performance that represents actual return on the investment.

Net present value is based on two principles: (1) a dollar today is worth more than a dollar in the future, and (2) higher risks require higher rewards. Net-present-value analysis compares the present value of the amount and timing of cash inflows of various projects to the present value of amount and timing of their cash outflows, applying a consistent discount or hurdle rate to represent the organization's return requirement over time. The basics of NPV analysis appear in Sidebar 6-2.

A project with a positive NPV represents an investment whose return is greater than the hurdle, because its inflows are greater than its outflows when all such flows are viewed in today's dollars and assuming a specified interest rate. In comparing two or more projects, the higher the project's NPV, the more attractive the project from a strictly financial perspective.

Four elements must be known to perform a valid NPV analysis: (1) an estimate of the amount and timing of up-front investment requirements, (2) the projection of free cash flows, (3) the organizational discount rate, and (4) the terminal value of the project. Descriptions of each follow.

Sidebar 6-2. Calculating Net Present Value

The future value of a present sum of money is expressed as $FV = PV(1+r)^t$ where:

$$FV = \text{Future value}$$
$$PV = \text{Present value}$$
$$r = \text{Interest rate}$$
$$t = \text{Number of time periods}$$

By rearranging the above terms, it is possible to express the present value of a future cash flow as follows:

$$PV = \frac{FV}{(1+r)^t}$$

The present value of an investment decision that results in a series of future cash flows may be expressed as follows:

$$NPV = C_0 + \frac{C_1}{(1+r)^t} + \frac{C_2}{(1+r)^2} + \frac{C_n}{(1+r)^n}$$

where

$$NPV = \text{Net present value}$$
$$C_0 = \text{Up-front expenditure associated with the investment}$$
$$C_0, C_2 \ldots C_n = \text{Particular cash flows expected in particular periods}$$
$$r = \text{Interest (or discount) rate}$$

As an example, assume that an invesment of $50 now would yield cash flows of $25 per year for three years and that the discount rate is 10 percent. The NPV of that investment would be:

$$(\$50) + \frac{\$25}{1.1} + \frac{\$25}{(1.1)^2} + \frac{\$25}{(1.1)^3} = (\$50) + \$23 + \$21 + \$19 = \$13$$

In corporate finance theory, the decision rule is that the investment is acceptable if it has a positive NPV, because this means that the investment generates more than the opportunity cost of capital.

Source: Reprinted from Kaufman, K. 2006. *Best-Practice Financial Management: Six Key Concepts for Healthcare Leaders*, 3rd ed. Chicago: Health Administration Press. Used with permission.

Up-Front Investment Requirements

An estimate of the amount and timing of project-related up-front investment should be reasonably clear if a proper business plan has been developed for the project. It is important that only incremental investment be included, ignoring outlays already made even if they are project related. These prior investments are, in effect, sunk costs (i.e., costs already incurred that remain unchanged regardless of any future project decision).

Organizations should be sure to include opportunity cost, however. Opportunity cost is defined as the difference in the benefits earned through investment in one use and the yield the capital could have earned, such as interest earnings, had it been placed in an alternative investment generating the highest possible yield. For example, a project proposal to construct a building on land that otherwise could be sold for a certain price should include the gain from the sale value of the land as an opportunity cost.

Requirements for working capital should be a final consideration in developing an estimate of total up-front investment. Initial funding requirements, such as start-up operating expense subsidies or support required until accounts receivable are collected, will need to be paid from cash reserves until the project is able to generate sufficient cash flow to carry these costs on its own.

Projection of Free Cash Flows

The projection of free cash flows involves determining how much cash will be generated in a particular year from the ongoing operation of the proposed project:

> Projected free cash flow = Projected net income + Depreciation
> – Projected increases in working capital requirements – Estimated capital expenditures

Appropriate free cash flow projections will *exclude* the following three categories of expense that would otherwise appear on a projected income statement:

1. *Depreciation:* This is a noncash expense item.
2. *Allocation of overhead:* By definition, overhead is fixed and is not incurred as a result of the proposed project; it exists in spite of the proposed project. If, however, a project truly creates an incremental change to overhead cost, only that increment should be included as an expense in free cash flow projections.
3. *Cost of capital (i.e., interest expense):* This exclusion reflects the basic tenet of corporate finance that mandates separation of investment decisions and financing decisions. Financing should be considered separately after a portfolio of projects has been identified, as described later in the chapter. Thus, projections of free cash flows essentially should assume that the project investment is 100 percent equity. Interest and/or principal payments should not be included in the projections.

Exclusions aside, organizations should remember to do the following:

- Explicitly estimate the incremental effects of factors, such as increased market share or operating efficiencies, attributed to the proposed investment
- Incorporate the effects of inflation on revenues and expenses
- Include the incremental ongoing capital requirements necessary to keep the project going

Organizational Discount Rate

The organizational discount rate determines the value of future cash flows relative to investment of like dollars today in interest-earning vehicles. If a project is risky, it should have a higher expected return than money invested in relatively risk-free investments. Key questions include How should the discount rate appropriate to an organization be established? How should the discounted cash flow analysis account for the relative risk of a particular investment?

A wide diversity of answers to these questions exists in both non-healthcare and healthcare organizations. A number of methods are often cited and used, but common to all methods is the conclusion that the real cost of capital to an organization is significantly higher than simply its cost of debt. Some people apply a rule of thumb that sets the discount rate at two times the risk-free rate (i.e., the interest rate on 30-year treasury bonds). Thus, if the current treasury rate is 5.35 percent, the applicable discount rate would be 10.7 percent.

Although rules of thumb may be straightforward and easy to apply, they do not provide the best approach to setting an appropriate discount or hurdle rate. To test the validity of an established hurdle rate, organizations should calculate the current operating EBITDA margin, defined as operating earnings before interest, taxes, depreciation, and amortization divided by total operating revenue. This ratio indicates the free cash flow return being generated by the organization's current operations and establishes a floor for future investment of capital. If current operations are generating X percent cash return, why should the organization settle for anything less from future invested capital?

Weighted average cost of capital (WACC) is used by the financial community as the most appropriate measure of the required return on capital for not-for-profit organizations. Although not-for-profit organizations do not return dividends to shareholders, they do need to generate enough capital to ensure ongoing reinvestment in growth and mission. Thus, the discount or hurdle rate should reflect the organization's WACC, which ensures reinvestment capital. Weighted average cost of capital is defined as the percentage of debt multiplied by the organization's cost of debt capital plus the percentage of equity multiplied by the equity's cost of capital. The WACC thus incorporates both cost of equity and cost of debt. It should be recalculated at least annually. Table 6-2 provides an illustration of how to calculate the WACC.

Terminal Value of a Project

The terminal value of a project is the estimate of that investment's value at the end of its operational life (i.e., the point at which significant additional capital investment will be required for the project to continue to generate cash flow). Terminal value often can account for 30 percent to 60 percent of

---

Table 6-2 Calculating the Weighted Average Cost of Capital

Equity Cost of Capital

Rf (risk-free rate)	5.09 %
ERP (equity risk premium)	7.08 %
ß (industry beta)	0.53
SP (size premium)	1.02 %
IP (tax-exempt illiquidity premium) = (Rf + [Rm–Rf]) × 20%	2.43 %
ARP (additional risk premium[s])	2.00 %
Re = Rf + (ß×ERP) + SP + IP + ARP	14.30 %

Debt Cost of Capital

Rd (estimated borrowing rate)	5.50 %
Estimated % debt in capital structure	43.00 %
Estimated % equity in capital structure	57.00 %
WACC = (% debt x debt cost of capital) + (% equity x equity cost of capital)	**10.51 %**

Note: This sample approach to the WACC calculation reflects a modification of the Capital Asset Pricing Model.

Source: Kaufman, Hall & Associates, Inc. Used with permission.

---

an investment's total value, and therefore it must be estimated carefully and documented thoroughly.

Terminal value can be estimated in four ways:

1. Assume *no value*, which would be appropriate for an item such as a computer that has no material value at the end of the project life.
2. Calculate *liquidation value*, based on the assumption that the asset has an anticipated sale value at the end of the project life.
3. Calculate an *annuity/perpetuity value*, which assumes that the investment will continue to generate free cash flow equal to that of the last year of the projection period during a period ranging from one year to forever.
4. Calculate a *growth perpetuity value*, which is similar to the annuity/perpetuity value but includes an assumption that the level of free cash flow after the projection period will change annually.

Remember that the terminal value of a project accrues at the end of the projection period. To define the true benefit of terminal value, the estimated future value must be discounted back to the beginning of the projection period using the discount rate applied to all other cash flows.

Other Issues Related to NPV Analysis

Additional issues associated with quantitative NPV analysis of proposed project investments include identifying project life and cash flow timing. Many organizations struggle with the following questions: What is the appropriate life of the project? Given the pace of change in healthcare and the breadth of unknown factors, is it possible to develop an analysis for a 10-year or 30-year project that is *at all* credible?

It should be noted that project life for NPV analysis purposes is not equal to the asset's depreciable life. For example, the depreciable life of a CT scanner may be seven years for accounting purposes. If an organization routinely operates such equipment for ten years, however, it would be appropriate to establish the project life for NPV purposes as ten years. If that is the case, however, increasing maintenance costs, down time, and clinical obsolescence should be reflected in the latter years of the cash flow projections. In this example, free cash flow will probably peak around the fifth year and decline, perhaps rapidly, during the subsequent years. Because the smaller cash flows in the latter years are discounted back to the present through the NPV analysis, the incremental impact of the extended life is likely to be minimal. A review of the organization's equipment-use history could help in establishing appropriate project lifespans.

The issue of project life is especially significant with multiyear construction projects. Because any incremental cash flows generated by the investment will not begin for several years, a short project life will invariably generate a negative NPV. On the other hand, assigning a 30-year project life, which may help support a positive NPV, also may create an unrealistically long time horizon for achieving an ROI. One potential approach to addressing this issue could be as simple as adding a fixed number of years (e.g., 15 years) to the project investment period to create a finite project life. In this way, even for a project with an extended construction period, the

NPV analysis provides for a sufficiently long operating period in which to evaluate net cash flows.

Expected cash flows and their timing should also be considered by organizations. When large projects are layered on top of one another, cash flow becomes critical. Multiple projects all with negative cash flows in their early years can sink an organization. Net-present-value analysis must be accompanied by an evaluation of the cash implications of the proposed project.

Considering Risk Through ENPV Analysis

The projections supporting NPV analysis are based on a set of planning assumptions that include incremental volume, revenue, expense, cost and revenue inflation, and cost of capital, all of which may or may not be accurate. If the assumptions are optimistic and overestimate the financial return of a project, the organization may be at considerable risk for overinvesting relative to its financial capability, which could lead to spending more capital than the organization can afford.

Net-present-value analysis can be made more powerful by integrating risk assessment techniques, such as Monte Carlo simulation, available with many software tools. Monte Carlo simulation bombards projections for an individual project or a portfolio of projects with a range of risk elements and generates a distribution of possible outcomes. Using simulation to further analyze projects creates a much more accurate estimate of the range of potential outcomes and therefore the risk-adjusted value of projects under consideration, or the ENPV.

For example, a hospital is thinking of investing in a new diagnostic imaging modality. The NPV of the project is estimated to be $585,882, based on the point estimate assumptions of incremental demand and operating costs and the resulting projections of cash flow (see Table 6-3). Although the NPV associated with the original point estimate is $585,882, this is not necessarily the risk-adjusted ENPV. Simulation will provide a range of NPV outcomes, applying randomly generated combinations of demand and operating assumptions, to create the ENPV. The ENPV provides an indication of the investment's likely return, incorporating risk, and illuminates potential hidden risks even for a project with a high NPV and ENPV.

Table 6-3. Net Present Value Computation

Projected Free Cash Flow Analysis

	2007	2008	2009	2010	2011	2012	2013
Income from operations	$0	$0	($51,811)	($178,923)	$271,149	$489,727	$743,512
Add back:							
Depreciation and amortization	0	0	180,214	365,786	371,143	376,500	381,857
Less:							
Ongoing capital needs	0	0	0	75,000	0	75,000	0
Working capital	0	0	36,815	12,656	62,570	35,169	40,778
Net free cash flow	$0	$0	$91,589	$ 99,207	$579,722	$756,057	$1,084,591

Net Present Value Computation

Year	Capital Investment	Initial Cash Flows	Project Cash Flows	Total Terminal Value	Discounted Cash Flow	Cumulative Discounted Cash Flow
2007	$0	$0	$0		$0	$0
2008	(2,025,000)	0	(2,025,000)		(2,025,000)	(2,025,000)
2009	(750,000)	91,589	(658,411)		(597,096)	(2,622,096)
2010	0	99,207	99,207		70,803	(2,551,294)
2011	0	579,722	579,722		369,743	(2,181,551)
2012	0	756,057	756,057		430,927	(1,750,623)
2013	0	1,084,591	1,084,591		552,441	(1,198,183)
Terminal Year				3,919,414	1,784,064	585,882
Total	($2,775,000)	$2,611,166	($163,834)	$3,919,414	$585,882	

Perpetuity cash flow change	0.0%
Total project life (in years)	10 years
Net present value of net free cash flow at 11.9%	**$585,882**

Source: Kaufman, Hall & Associates, Inc. Used with permission.

The simulation in the current example indicates that the diagnostic imaging modality could have an NPV ranging from in excess of positive $500,000 to as low as negative $600,000. Figure 6-2 shows that the ENPV (the mean NPV of the range of possible outcomes) for the project is $122,000. This means that the project still has a positive return, given consideration of all potential

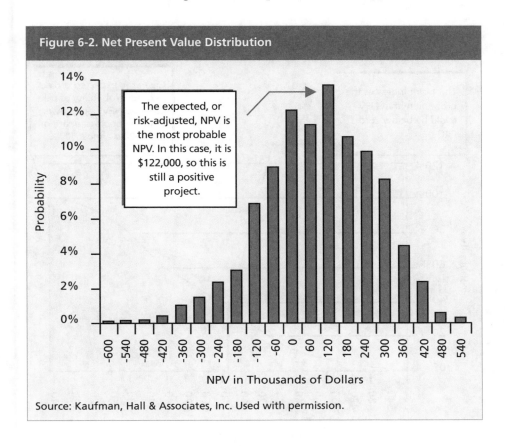

Figure 6-2. Net Present Value Distribution

The expected, or risk-adjusted, NPV is the most probable NPV. In this case, it is $122,000, so this is still a positive project.

NPV in Thousands of Dollars

Source: Kaufman, Hall & Associates, Inc. Used with permission.

risks and the impact of those risks on the range of assumptions generating the free cash flow projections. However, it also indicates that those risks will reduce the probability of generating the $585,882 point estimate cash flows projected in the standard NPV analysis. Using the imaging modality's ENPV, leaders can better compare this initiative with other initiatives under consideration.

Another view of the range of possible outcomes shows a slightly different picture of the investment. Figure 6-3 essentially is Figure 6-2 turned on its side to present the cumulative effect of the individual NPV probabilities. It indicates that there is approximately a 38 percent probability that the diagnostic imaging modality could bring a negative NPV and an almost 100 percent probability that the project will actually generate cash flows less than the point estimate projection. In other words, when risk is included in the analysis, it is clear that there is virtually no chance of achieving the NPV of $585,000.

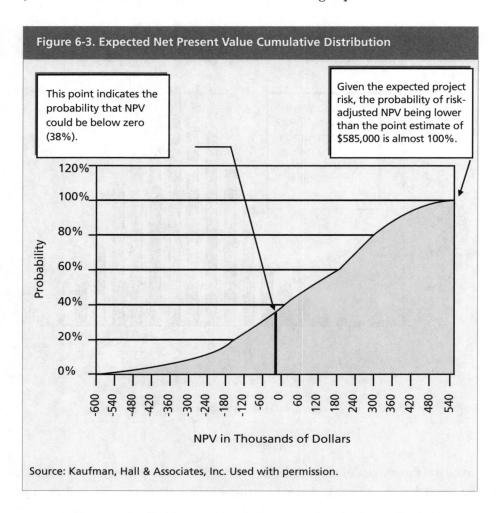

Figure 6-3. Expected Net Present Value Cumulative Distribution

This point indicates the probability that NPV could be below zero (38%).

Given the expected project risk, the probability of risk-adjusted NPV being lower than the point estimate of $585,000 is almost 100%.

Probability

NPV in Thousands of Dollars

Source: Kaufman, Hall & Associates, Inc. Used with permission.

Risk adjustment, also known as *sensitivity analysis*, should be consistently applied to all threshold capital projects. The analysis should reflect the specific risk parameters applicable to the project-related assumptions.

For example, one hospital established a policy to assess the potential risk associated with each threshold capital project by estimating high and low assumption ranges for the following categories, as appropriate:

- Incremental project-related volume
- Incremental project-related revenue
- Reimbursement inflation by payer type

- Beginning salary levels by FTE type
- Annual salary inflation levels
- Annual variable expense inflation levels
- Annual fixed expense inflation levels
- Initial capital investment requirements
- Growth/decrease in annual perpetuity cash flow levels

The upside and downside scenarios made visible with this kind of sensitivity analysis can be significant and dramatic. Using Monte Carlo simulation, Figure 6-4 (a "tornado graph") focuses on the identified risk components and their relative contribution to driving the projected ENPV of the diagnostic imaging modality example.

The figure provides valuable information to both the project sponsor and the capital management council. Clearly, the project's highest risk is associated with changes in future reimbursement inflation. The reimbursement inflation bar's extension to the right of zero indicates a positive and direct correlation between higher inflation (i.e., higher net revenue) and higher project NPV. Additionally, the graph highlights the significant negative correlation between capital investment and NPV. While this relationship may seem obvious, capital investment in many organizations is one of the least challenged assumptions of project proposals, in spite of the fact that reduction in capital investment requirements has a dollar-for-dollar positive impact on project NPV.

The positive correlation between discharges and NPV, as opposed to the lack of correlation between procedural volumes and NPV, indicates that the ancillary service provision, as structured in the proposal, is not profitable. The project relies on inpatient referrals to generate cash flow. This insight provided by the tornado graph signals management's need to carefully assess the proposed operating structure of the project to determine if changes can be made to enhance cash flows, mitigate project risk, and maximize potential project return.

The industrywide increase in large capital projects, such as replacement facilities, with multiyear up-front investments and limited short-term returns, has highlighted the need for increased analysis of project risk and the comparative risk of multiple projects. The traditional approach of creating optimistic, pessimistic, and expected scenarios is no longer sufficient

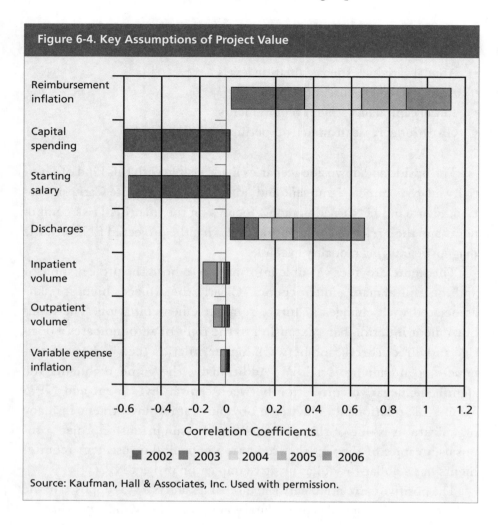

Figure 6-4. Key Assumptions of Project Value

Source: Kaufman, Hall & Associates, Inc. Used with permission.

to provide the necessary understanding of potential risk factors and their quantifiable effects. To support its evaluation of alternative investments selected to create a comprehensive capital portfolio, the council needs to address questions such as the following:

- How are project risk factors identified?
- What are the best approaches to quantifying risk for various project types?
- Should risk be evaluated on a project-specific basis or through the use of broad risk factors?
- Should target rates of return be changed to reflect risk?

- Should project risk in a stand-alone hospital be assessed by departments or the hospital as a whole?
- Should project risk in a health system be assessed by individual hospitals or by the corporate organization as a whole?

Understanding the risk parameters of a project or a portfolio of projects through the use of ENPV as the ROI method of choice will enable healthcare leaders to make high-quality decisions regarding which investments to pursue.

Qualitative Analysis

While quantitative analysis focuses on margin, qualitative analysis focuses on issues that are more difficult to quantify, including mission; consistency with the strategic plan; community needs; and effect on patient and staff safety, quality, physician alignment, innovation, customer value, and process improvement. By definition, qualitative evaluation is subjective and reflects the experience and perspective of each individual evaluator at one point in time, even when performed concurrently by dozens of individuals.

Qualitative measures that are more objective in nature should be included in an organization's initial project-screening criteria. Such measures include the following:

- *Consistency with the organization's mission, vision, and values:* Is the initiative compatible in these domains?
- *Consistency with the organization's stated strategic plan:* Does the initiative fit with the plan or not?

These are yes/no questions that should be simple to answer. A "yes" response means that the project should be retained on the list; a "no" answer should result in demotion of the proposed investment to the bottom of the list. If the question generates a lot of discussion, the organization's leaders may be trying to bend the initiative or the organization's stated mission, vision, values, and strategic plan to achieve a fit for a favored project.

Other qualitative criteria will vary by organization. Executives should identify and agree on the criteria that will be used to evaluate potential

---

Sidebar 6-3. Sample Criteria and Related Questions for Threshold Projects

Outcomes/Satisfaction
How important is this project to patient clinical outcomes? How important is the project to physician, employee, and patient satisfaction?

Operating Efficiency
Will this project result in the following types of efficiencies?
- Increased patient throughput
- Decreased length of stay
- Enhanced seamlessness of patient care
- Enhanced interdepartmental cooperation
- Decreased administrative burden

Infrastructure Quality
Will this project improve the appearance and/or functionality of the facility? Will the project improve the availability or timeliness of critical information? Will the project increase the level of coordination between the hospital and its partners (for example, physician practices, the school of medicine, and the university)? Will the project improve the hospital's image and reputation? Will the project result in increased market share or strengthen the network of referrals?

Return on Investment
This criterion will be scored by the health system finance department and will be based on the project's ability to return the original cost of the project.

Source: The University of Kansas Hospital, Kansas City, Kansas. Used with permission.

---

initiatives; all proposed projects should be evaluated based on these criteria. Sidebar 6-3 provides the criteria and related questions used by an academic medical center in the Midwest.

Criteria Weighting

Because evaluation of qualitative criteria often consumes a disproportionate amount of time, organizations frequently find it helpful to put in

Table 6-4. Qualitative Criteria and Criteria Weighting Example

Criteria	Weighting
Safety and quality	30%
Physician alignment	20%
Customer value	20%
Process improvement	15%
Growth of mission	10%
Innovation	5%

place a scoring system that weights qualitative measures. Establishing these criteria and their relative weighting must be the domain of the council and must be explicitly agreed upon by the council members. These items are always organization specific.

Qualitative assessment using weighted criteria may be the responsibility of the individuals bringing forward projects to the council or, alternatively, may be solely the council's responsibility following review and presentation of all projects. Some organizations combine both of these approaches very effectively. As an example, one hospital's capital management council defined the criteria identified in Table 6-4 and their relative weights. Note that "financial return" is not included on this list. This was done specifically to separate the purely quantitative and objective context of the NPV analysis from the qualitative factors.

After completing the quantitative and qualitative analyses described in this chapter, an organization's capital management council is properly equipped to select a high-quality portfolio of threshold projects. Chapter Seven addresses this selection process.

References

Kaufman, K. 2003. In "The Value of Healthcare Information Technology." *hfm/JHIM*. Special advertising section, January, 3–31.

Malehorn, J. E. 2005. In "Seven Principles of Best-Practice Financial Management." Financing the Future II Series. Westchester, IL: Healthcare Financial Management Association.

CHAPTER SEVEN

Using a Portfolio Approach to Threshold Project Selection

THIS CHAPTER DESCRIBES how organizations combine the information obtained through quantitative and qualitative analyses, as described in Chapter Six, to select a portfolio of threshold projects that balances margin and mission. The process begins with a quantitatively based ranking, integrates qualitatively based data, and then unites both analyses to make a final selection of threshold projects.

Quantitative Project Ranking

The traditional way to select projects from a purely quantitative view is to rank them in priority order, placing the project with the highest NPV or ENPV first, followed by projects of lesser NPV or ENPV in descending order.

According to this approach, all projects with a positive NPV/ENPV whose total capital costs do not exceed the defined capital constraint are selected; those projects appearing lower on the list after the capital constraint has been exceeded and projects with a negative NPV/ENPV are not approved. Ranking projects by NPV has been a core practice of corporate-style capital allocation and management since the 1950s.

In healthcare, especially not-for-profit healthcare, exclusive reliance on financial return as the decision-making criterion is very rare. Most healthcare organizations include financial return as a key criterion among other decision-making criteria. The weighting of criteria importance varies by organization and often is more implicit than explicit. Some organizations establish a weighting system that effectively combines quantitative and qualitative analyses to capture mission, strategy, and financial issues in a composite ranking.

An effective decision-making procedure highlights the financial implications of qualitatively (i.e., subjective) driven decisions by maintaining a list of all proposed projects in a complete table sorted in descending order of NPV or ENPV. By maintaining such a table, the potential financial impact of alternative council-allocation decisions remains transparent and allows the organization to consider the list as a whole, as described later. As each set of projects is approved, the council can determine whether the list has a positive or negative NPV, thereby adding to or detracting from the organization's long-term value.

Figure 7-1 shows one organization's ranking list. It indicates that the total portfolio NPV of the top 11 proposed projects, fundable within its $16 million capital constraint and sorted solely on the basis of the NPV analysis, is $34.2 million. In a *Fortune* 100 company, this list would represent the capital allocated for the coming year. Decisions in a not-for-profit healthcare organization, however, are not so cut and dry. Management must also consider qualitative factors.

Integrating Qualitative Information

In Chapter Six, an organization's council identified qualitative criteria and the appropriate weighting of such criteria (refer to Table 6-4). Based on these criteria, the council is now ready to integrate qualitative factors.

To do so, team members vote individually on the 15 projects itemized in Figure 7-1. The combined voting scores establish each project's weighted qualitative ranking within the total portfolio of potential projects under consideration (Figure 7-2). This ranking may be considerably different from the NPV ranking illustrated in Figure 7-1. In fact, it is entirely possible that

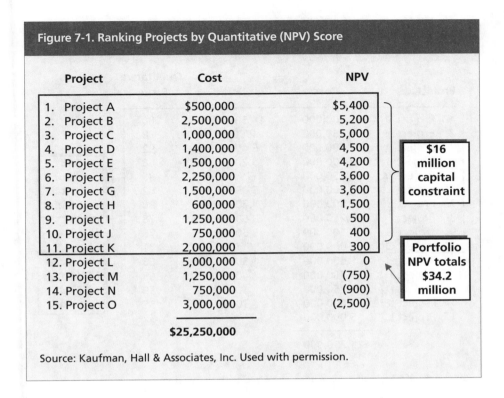

Figure 7-1. Ranking Projects by Quantitative (NPV) Score

Project	Cost	NPV	
1. Project A	$500,000	$5,400	
2. Project B	2,500,000	5,200	
3. Project C	1,000,000	5,000	
4. Project D	1,400,000	4,500	$16 million capital constraint
5. Project E	1,500,000	4,200	
6. Project F	2,250,000	3,600	
7. Project G	1,500,000	3,600	
8. Project H	600,000	1,500	
9. Project I	1,250,000	500	
10. Project J	750,000	400	
11. Project K	2,000,000	300	
12. Project L	5,000,000	0	Portfolio NPV totals $34.2 million
13. Project M	1,250,000	(750)	
14. Project N	750,000	(900)	
15. Project O	3,000,000	(2,500)	

$25,250,000

Source: Kaufman, Hall & Associates, Inc. Used with permission.

projects with negative NPVs will appear at the top on the list of projects that would be selected solely according to their qualitative scores.

Note how the inclusion of projects with lower NPVs, including those with negative NPVs, reduces the overall NPV for the portfolio of projects from $34.2 million to $27.35 million. If the council selected projects based solely on qualitative criteria, which is not the recommended approach, it would effectively be leaving approximately $7 million of potential value on the table.

In fact, some organizations could conceivably complete both the quantitative and qualitative analyses and rankings and decide to select projects based solely on the qualitative rankings, leaving the $7 million on the table. Such decisions, in fact, may have been made in the past without a structured capital decision-making process but without being visible to the rest of the organization. With a best-practice process, these decisions must be made consciously and are communicated, thereby becoming

Figure 7-2. Ranking Projects by Qualitative Score

Project	Cost	NPV	Qualitative Score	
1. Project D	$1,400,000	$4,500	100	
2. Project N	750,000	(900)	98	
3. Project A	500,000	5,400	92	
4. Project B	2,500,000	5,200	88	$16 million capital constraint
5. Project M	1,250,000	(750)	85	
6. Project C	1,000,000	5,000	82	
7. Project E	1,500,000	4,200	80	
8. Project F	2,250,000	3,600	78	
9. Project G	1,500,000	3,600	76	
10. Project O	3,000,000	(2,500)	71	
11. Project H	600,000	1,500	68	Portfolio NPV totals $27.35 million
12. Project J	750,000	400	63	
13. Project I	1,250,000	500	59	
14. Project K	2,000,000	300	55	
15. Project L	5,000,000	0	52	
	$25,250,000			

Source: Kaufman, Hall & Associates, Inc. Used with permission.

transparent to the entire organization. The council would need to justify its acceptance of a capital portfolio with reduced economic benefit to the organization.

Balancing Margin and Mission

Best-practice capital decision making involves balancing margin and mission—the quantitative and qualitative factors assessed up to this point. This may not be an easy process either financially or politically.

The key to appropriate allocation lies in maintaining a portfolio approach, which has three critical and often conflicting objectives:

1. To protect the organization's mission and community initiatives;
2. To quantify the potential impact of qualitatively based decisions; and

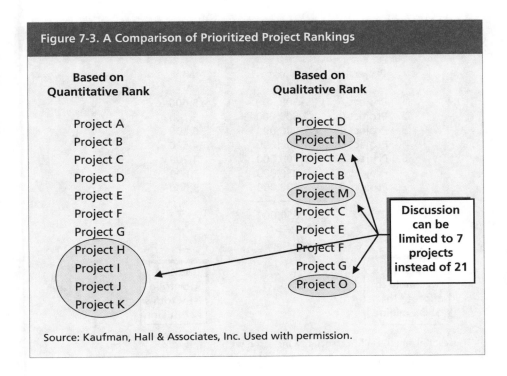

Figure 7-3. A Comparison of Prioritized Project Rankings

Source: Kaufman, Hall & Associates, Inc. Used with permission.

3. To ensure that total capital investment will generate sufficient returns and cash flows to meet the organization's short-term needs and create long-term value.

An organization's council must provide structure for the portfolio review and comparison process, focusing on areas of inconsistency between qualitative evaluation and quantitative evaluation. The council also must quantify the value of a proposed capital portfolio to assess the organization's ability to meet the associated capital requirements. The council needs a means to assess, on a real-time basis, the impact of proposed changes to the portfolio.

To focus on areas of inconsistency, the council can place side-by-side the qualitatively and quantitatively ranked lists of the projects that could be approved within the capital constraint (see Figure 7-3). Although 21 projects originally were submitted, only 11 now appear on the quantitative ranking and 10 appear on the qualitative ranking. Projects A through G appear on both lists because they have met both quantitative and qualitative criteria. These projects should not require further discussion; they should be allocated capital by

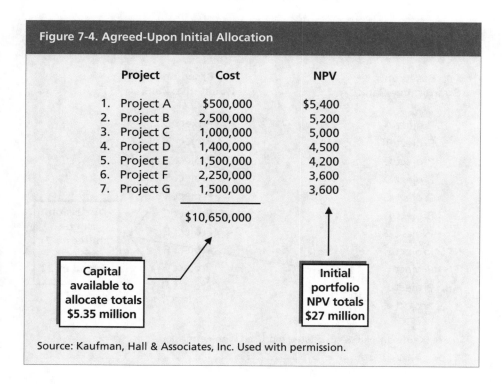

Figure 7-4. Agreed-Upon Initial Allocation

Project	Cost	NPV
1. Project A	$500,000	$5,400
2. Project B	2,500,000	5,200
3. Project C	1,000,000	5,000
4. Project D	1,400,000	4,500
5. Project E	1,500,000	4,200
6. Project F	2,250,000	3,600
7. Project G	1,500,000	3,600
	$10,650,000	

Capital available to allocate totals $5.35 million

Initial portfolio NPV totals $27 million

Source: Kaufman, Hall & Associates, Inc. Used with permission.

the council. In fact, council discussion should focus on the seven projects—H, I, J, K, N, M, and O—that appear only on one of the lists, instead of the originally submitted 21 projects or the 11 projects represented on the quantitative and qualitative project rankings.

As Figure 7-4 illustrates, $10.65 million of the total $16 million capital constraint for threshold capital will be allocated to projects A through G, which have a portfolio NPV value of $27 million. This means that available capital for the remaining seven projects is only $5.35 million. Furthermore, because the NPV for the initially approved projects is $27 million, the remaining projects under discussion could have a combined negative NPV (of up to $27 million) and still create a balanced portfolio.

In this example, there is no combination of remaining projects that could create such a negative NPV. The lowest NPV possible, given the remaining available capital constraint, would be negative $4.15 million. Regardless, the council should approve additional projects that minimize the negative economic consequences for the organization, especially

Figure 7-5. Allocating the Remaining Capital

Project	Cost	NPV	Qualitative Score
1. Project H	$600,000	$1,500	68
2. Project I	1,250,000	500	59
3. Project J	750,000	400	63
4. Project K	2,000,000	300	55
5. Project M	1,250,000	(750)	85
6. Project N	750,000	(900)	98
7. Project O	3,000,000	(2,500)	71
	$9,600,000		

Source: Kaufman, Hall & Associates, Inc. Used with permission.

given the limited capital investment ($5.35 million) that would create that outcome.

How should the council allocate the remaining $5.35 million? Figure 7-5 shows that the total investment in the seven projects—$9.6 million—would exceed available capital, so choices clearly need to be made. Selecting the projects with the highest qualitative scores—M, N, and O—would not exceed the available capital but would result in reducing the portfolio's total NPV by more than $4 million. Selecting the projects with positive NPVs— H, I, J, and K—also would not exceed available capital and would contribute $2.7 million to the portfolio's NPV.

In this example, either decision could be supported given the strength of the remaining projects in the portfolio. Nonetheless, the final decisions about project selection should be made in a transparent way, enabling management to reinforce support for all aspects of the organization's strategy.

As described in Chapter Two, the organization's capital management council is the linchpin to an effective process for managing capital, especially as it relates to threshold capital projects. Strong centralized management seeks to discourage the conditions under which allocation of capital devolves into a free for all. Political clout, timing (first to the trough), and access to senior management must not influence decision making; decisions must be based on a real analysis of what is good for the organization.

As described in Chapter Three through Chapter Seven, the council must work within a highly structured process to calculate the organization's weighted average cost of capital, identify the capital constraint, quantify carry-forward capital, determine the allocation of the capital constraint between the threshold and nonthreshold pools, allocate the nonthreshold capital pool to operating units, and allocate threshold capital to a portfolio of projects that ensures continued competitive financial performance. Chapter Eight describes the process used by the council following its selection of a portfolio of threshold projects.

CHAPTER 8

The Post-Allocation Process

A BEST-PRACTICE capital management process does not end when allocation decisions are made. Rather, a post-allocation process commences. This process includes review and revalidation of projects before the actual funding, decision making regarding the timing of capital spending, handling of any budget deficits or surpluses that occur, ongoing monitoring of capital spending, and determining the appropriate course of action based on performance results. A discussion of these topics follows.

Funding Review/Revalidation

Best-practice capital management requires some form of revalidation of project parameters before final approval and funding of allocated capital. This ensures that new data or information obtained *following* the project's approval can be taken into account and integrated appropriately.

Many organizations require project sponsors to update the threshold capital project-approval form originally submitted to the capital management council to support the revalidation process. According to these organizations, the standardized form helps to ensure that sponsors provide the information needed for decision making at the time of both allocation and revalidation. The same data and analysis that supported the original allocation

III

decision will support the project's revalidation. Some of the project parameters may have changed in the months since initial evaluation of the capital request. Information captured through the form enables such changes to be identified and evaluated.

Some hospitals and health systems consider allocation decisions as unalterable. All approved projects receive funding. Other organizations are more willing to revisit the allocation decision at the funding point. In the extreme version of this approach, allocation decision-making and funding decision making are so separate that two allocation/approval processes exist. In such a situation, a project sponsor shepherds the project through the extensive batch allocation process before the start of the year but really has no assurance that allocated capital ultimately will be made available. This undermines the integrity of the initial allocation decision, extends the decision-making time frame, and increases the potential for politics to creep back into the decision process. Clearly, the revalidation process must provide a reaffirmation, based on updated information, that the project for which capital has been allocated remains essentially the same.

In the best-practice allocation process defined in earlier chapters, threshold capital requests with costs above a defined dollar level undergo an analytically rigorous review at the time of allocation decision making. Analytically rigorous revalidation before funding also is typically limited to threshold capital requests. The council assumes responsibility for this revalidation function.

Figure 8-1 illustrates how revalidation fits into an integrated process. At some point in time following the formal allocation of capital, the project sponsor initiates the revalidation process by submitting a request to obtain funding approval. This occurs at some point during the fiscal year for which the allocation has been made (the allocation year). Specific timing for this funding request will vary by project and by organization. In some cases, revalidation by the council will occur at the point of contract execution but could be earlier, such as when detailed drawings for a new construction project are finalized. To some extent, this is a function of organizational culture. Some organizational councils require virtually complete information to approve funding; other councils delegate project finalization to the sponsor within broad parameters. With either approach, the council assumes responsibility for moving the funding request forward.

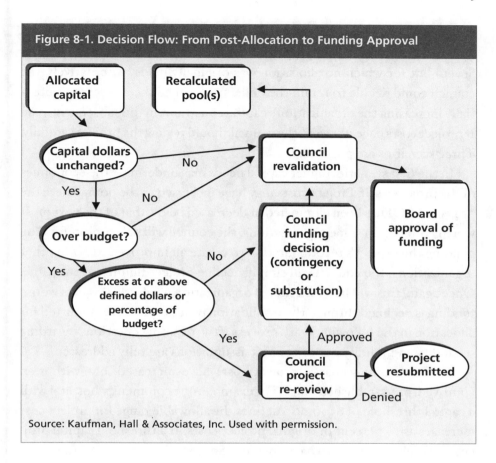

Figure 8-1. Decision Flow: From Post-Allocation to Funding Approval

Source: Kaufman, Hall & Associates, Inc. Used with permission.

The scope of revalidation for approved threshold capital projects must be well defined. Through the allocation decision-making process, the council has already confirmed the project's strategic necessity and economic appropriateness. The revalidation process should not be viewed as another chance to take a shot at the project's validity. Rather, revalidation should verify that the original project premise is still valid, that the key assumptions continue to be supported, and, most importantly, that the capital associated with the project is consistent with the original submission.

If there is *no change* in project-related capital cost, or the capital cost has *decreased*, the project remains valid. In the case of decreased costs, the council should validate the new cost figure and return the unneeded capital to the organizational contingency pool for future application as determined by the council. If the repatriated dollars are significant, the council can also decide to allocate some of the dollars to the project that appears as the next priority on the capital list (compiled through the process described in Chapter Seven) but for which no allocation was originally made. Alternatively, the council could decide to retain the dollars as balance sheet reserves, potentially increasing the organization's capital constraint in the subsequent year. If project costs have *increased*, the council should review the project carefully. Three scenarios are possible.

In the first scenario, higher capital needs may undermine the economics of the project itself. Project costs may have increased to the point where the projected ROI has been eliminated or decreased below that of the next most worthy project. In some organizations, the council will halt project funding pending the project's reconfiguration to create an improved ROI. In other organizations, the council will simply decline project funding at this time. Once again, this will be a function of organizational culture. Projects whose funding is declined through the revalidation process can be resubmitted for allocation in the following year's process *if* the resulting questions regarding reliability and validity of project cost assumptions are fully addressed.

In the second scenario, project costs have increased, but within an approved, pre-established range. For example, one community hospital with a capital threshold of $500,000 defines the allowable range for project cost increases as 10 percent of original project costs. If a threshold capital project originally projected to have costs of $800,000 has costs of $840,000 at the revalidation stage, the council would move the project forward for funding approval. The council also would allocate dollars from the contingency pool to cover the additional $40,000 costs. Should contingency dollars not be available, the council would then be forced to decide whether to stop the project or fund it by deferring another project for which funds have already been allocated.

In the third scenario, project costs have increased beyond the pre-established range, but not high enough to negatively affect the project's ROI. Given its previous approval of the project's strategic necessity and appropriateness, the council would move the project forward for funding and determine the source of the required additional capital.

One very important point to note: this revalidation process, like the original allocation and capital budget process, does nothing to diminish the board's role in capital approval. If anything, this best-practice structure improves the board's ability to perform its duties. When a specific capital project is brought by the council to the board for final approval (i.e., funding), the board has the assurance that the project has been thoroughly and consistently analyzed by the council, has been established as a priority strategic investment for the organization, and has been vetted for any material changes that would affect the direction of the original allocation (budgeting) decision. The board, of course, would have already seen the project as part of the recommended capital budget and would be aware of its imminent funding requirement. The board will also have a complete understanding of the source of funding for the project, including whether or not the project is using funds from the contingency pool.

Timing of Capital Spending

The council also manages the overall schedule under which allocated threshold capital projects are funded. The organization's finance team supports this function by providing the council with anticipated cash flow schedules on a quarter-by-quarter basis.

In some organizations, the council also manages nonthreshold capital spending by releasing nonthreshold dollars on a quarterly basis subject to the organization's achievement of agreed-upon operating performance levels. This degree of oversight is less common, especially in multihospital systems, but does provide for corporate-level management of spending to ensure appropriate matching of operating performance with capital expenditure levels. It also ensures that the organization will not run out of available nonthreshold capital dollars before year end.

One approach to the management of the nonthreshold pool is to release a portion of the total dollar allocation in each of the first three quarters. Assuming the council meets on a quarterly basis, this is manageable and provides the council with the ability to increase the size of the nonthreshold capital pool should the organization's performance be significantly better than planned.

Management of threshold capital projects is somewhat more straightforward. At the time of allocation, the council will have ranked the threshold capital projects according to priority—based on both quantitative and qualitative factors—and will have built a related cash flow schedule covering the upcoming allocation year. Thus, the council can proactively manage the release of capital for spending based on the original project ranking and anticipated project timing.

The project investment cash flow schedule should reflect the organization's current and projected cash flow position by fiscal quarter. In addition, the cash flow projections need to be continually updated to enable control of the release of cash for capital projects as a function of organizational performance. In this way, the council can use actual quarterly operating cash flow results to drive release of funds as follows:

- If operating cash flow is *below* plan, implementation of approved threshold and nonthreshold capital projects should be proportionately reduced. Threshold capital reductions would begin with the lowest-ranked projects scheduled for the last quarter.
- If operating cash flow *exceeds* plan, options available to the council include
  o   approving additional threshold capital in the fourth quarter;
  o   approving increased nonthreshold capital levels for the third and fourth quarters; or
  o   retaining the cash on the organization's balance sheet to carry over to the next year through an increased capital constraint.

If the council determines that the organization has insufficient capital capacity because of material operating under performance, the spending on threshold capital projects may need to be deferred to a specific quarter or even into the subsequent year. Any such changes to initial allocations or project timing should be based on review of the organization's and/or operating entity's financial performance relative to the plan on which the capital constraint was based.

Mid-year financial performance is particularly critical because at the end of two full quarters, a true picture of the organization's current-year financial trajectory can be developed. At the mid-year point, the council can best determine whether the funding needs and capital availability for the organization, in fact, will be in balance. If balance is not present, the council should be empowered to make appropriate adjustments to third-quarter and fourth-quarter spending.

The council also should establish a policy regarding how to handle capital that has been allocated but has been deferred because of adjustments to account for operating performance of the organization as a whole. An example of such a policy follows:

- Nonthreshold capital spending that is deferred by the council because of determination of insufficient organizational capital capacity may, at the discretion of the operating entity management team, be funded through the subsequent year's nonthreshold capital allocation or through the threshold capital review process, as appropriate.
- Threshold capital projects that are deferred by the council because of the determination of insufficient organizational capital capacity will be considered carry-forward capital and will be managed under the policy governing that type of capital as part of the subsequent year's capital management process.

Deferral of capital spending because of underperformance is a serious issue with serious consequences. As reflected in these policy statements, best-practice capital management does not give the deferred threshold capital request a pass; there is no tacit approval or additional capital made available to fund these capital items. They essentially become part of the standard capital management process in the subsequent year. The underlying reason for the deferral—underperformance—must be acknowledged and addressed.

Unspent Allocated Capital

On occasion, threshold capital projects may not end up requiring as much money as was projected at the time of allocation. This may be evident when funding approval is sought or on actual completion of the project. Policies established and implemented by the council should address unspent capital for both threshold and nonthreshold capital projects. This will ensure that departments within a hospital or hospitals within a system do not revert to the political allocation of leftover funds and convert funds allocated for one purpose to another.

Policies related to unspent allocated capital should address the following:

- At the conclusion of a threshold capital project, unspent capital should not be transferred to another project or spent in any other manner. This allocated capital must be returned to the contingency pool to be reallocated in either the current or future years, as determined by the council.
- Allocated nonthreshold capital that is not spent at the conclusion of a fiscal year should not be transferred to the subsequent year. Rather, the allocated dollars should be returned to the organizational balance sheet, mitigating the need to build cash-reserve levels and increasing the subsequent year's capital constraint.

For example, a department manager who receives approval in October for a $500,000 project determines in July of the following year that the contracts required for the initiative total $450,000. The manager returns $50,000 to the capital pool for reallocation by the council as either threshold or nonthreshold capital.

For some organizations, the nonthreshold policy component discussed here raises concerns about creating a use-it-or-lose-it mentality. Essentially, the policy says that unspent nonthreshold capital allocated to an operating unit will revert back to the organization at year end. To alleviate this concern, these organizations may permit controlled carry forward of nonthreshold capital spending; these dollars can be spent in the first quarter of the following year. Under any circumstances, it is in the organization's best interest to minimize nonthreshold carry-forward capital. The more significant this carry forward becomes, the more difficult it is to establish a finite capital constraint. The carry forward is essentially a contingent liability; there is no way to know what portion of it will actually be spent.

Emergency and Off-Cycle Capital Requests

Success of the best-practice, one time, batch capital management process depends on ensuring only a very limited number of emergency and off-cycle capital requests. Organizations should define the emergency capital and off-cycle capital requests that can be considered outside of the annual batch process and specify the required approval procedures. For example, a children's hospital defined each as follows:

- *Emergency capital* is defined as unanticipated capital needs for facility code violations or equipment failure that will materially affect a core business or quality of patient care. The policy is as follows:
  o Nonthreshold emergency capital follows the decentralized capital authorization process with funding through substitution or from contingency reserves at the department or operating-entity level.
  o Threshold emergency capital requires council approval with funding from the organization's contingency pool and/or through threshold capital project substitution, as necessary and determined by the council.
- *Off-cycle capital* is defined as nonemergent and truly unforeseen capital needs that management feels cannot wait for the next planning cycle. The policy includes the same review, approval, and funding processes as with emergency capital.

Experience indicates that off-cycle/emergency capital needs are actually relatively rare occurrences; the policy should not encourage such requests.

Requests for off-cycle capital from individuals who are basically trying to "game" the process by claiming off-cycle status for capital needs that simply exceed the available allocation should be denied promptly and consistently. In addition, off-cycle, incremental allocation of threshold or nonthreshold capital should under no circumstance be made to operating entities that spend allocated capital before year end, unless the council has complete confidence that a specific request for emergency or off-cycle capital is valid.

Application of Contingency Dollars

The council should have sole authority over use of contingency pool dollars, the total of which is defined as part of the calculation of net capital available for spending—the capital constraint, described in Chapter Three. Use of the contingency pool should be reserved for emergency and off-cycle capital requests, funding of budget overruns, and support of the organization's capital needs if organizational financial performance falls significantly short of planned levels.

The council should define a specific time each year—most often the end of the second quarter—to assess financial performance and the possible need to release contingency pool dollars to either the threshold or nonthreshold pool. For example, if the organization's financial performance (i.e., profitability and cash flow) is at or above plan at the end of the second quarter of the fiscal year, the council (and only the council) should have the discretion to release contingency dollars. Such release would clearly be based on comprehensive cash flow projections and review of outstanding, potential threshold capital needs.

Continuous Project Monitoring

Post-approval review and monitoring is vital to the integrity of the capital management process. Successful healthcare organizations define quantifiable indicators of project success, measure performance against these indicators, and devise and implement plans to respond to less-than-anticipated performance (Grube and Wareham 2005).

Ongoing measurement of actual investment performance must be built into both the governance and the calendar of the capital management process. Such measurement provides credibility, enabling specific comparison of actual results to projected results. Post-project monitoring helps ensure that cost and revenue projections are both on target and reasonable. Furthermore, with measurement, individuals know they will be held accountable for performance results. The presence of ongoing monitoring ultimately improves the quality of up-front analysis performed and helps ensure realistic forecasts and assumptions. Knowing that a project's performance will be reviewed in the future keeps managers and executives from providing overly aggressive or unsupported cash flow estimates.

Ongoing measurement also provides a means for transferring knowledge about investment success or failure throughout the organization. It creates a historical track record and corporate memory, and it also provides lessons learned about particular kinds of projects and whether and how they performed relative to expectations. This enables executives to be much smarter about the rightness of assumptions the next time a similar project is on the table.

The council should define the post-allocation monitoring time frame for the review of every approved threshold capital project. For example, one organization might establish guidelines that indicate the following:

> Threshold capital projects, including projects in which operations begin in the first investment year and multiyear projects in which operations do not begin in the first investment year, would be reviewed by the council annually until after the project has completed one full year of operations.

In this organization, projects with a long build-out or start-up period could be required to undergo annual review for several years.

Post-allocation, retrospective analysis should mirror the prospective analysis prepared in support of the original allocation decision. Benchmarks and metrics related to both qualitative and quantitative aspects of the project should be based on the benchmarks and metrics used in the project's business plan.

In fact, it may be appropriate to employ a project tracking form structured identically to the capital request form used by the council to make allocation decisions. The point of such standardization is that when a project sponsor understands that any assumption made in the allocation process will become a metric used for performance evaluation, the benchmarks employed become more distinct, quantifiable, and measurable. From an organizational standpoint, this means better up-front analysis and better capability to manage and assess post-allocation project performance. Table 8-1 illustrates a post-allocation tracking form.

Responding to Performance Results

Best-practice capital management and monitoring requires more than simply the development of data collection and analysis requirements. Organizations also need to determine what they are going to do with the information about a project that is not meeting performance targets established in the business

Table 8-1. Post-Allocation Tracking Form

Project Name	Original Budget	Transfers	Adjusted Budget	Funded	Remaining Funds	Current Request	Actual Spent	Funded vs. Actual Variance
Cancer center trailer	$ 28,000	$ 0	$ 28,000	$ 28,000	$ 0	$ 0	$ 27,482	$ 518
Radiology angio suite B remodel	9,000	0	9,000	9,000	0	6,000	8,592	408
New MRI scanner	1,525,000	0	1,525,000	100,000	1,425,000	115,000	98,000	2,000
Optical storage scanner	53,500	(5,000)	48,500	52,350	(3,850)	0	0	52,350
Optical disk storage drive	32,100	0	32,100	0	32,100	0	0	0
Surgical gamma probe	75,660	(1,000)	74,660	73,600	1,060	0	68,000	5,600
New PC desktops	7,704	1,000	8,704	0	8,704	0	0	0
Triage EKG machines	30,388	(7,888)	22,500	22,500	0	0	24,000	(1,500)
I-stat analyzer	8,807	2,888	11,695	10,000	1,695	0	0	10,000
Sterilizing equipment—new	0	5,000	5,000	5,000	0	0	0	5,000
Vital signs monitor	7,954	0	7,954	5,000	2,954	0	0	5,000
Flooring and millwork	34,750	0	34,750	15,625	19,125	5,550	15,536	89
Playroom equipment	18,655	0	18,655	5,000	13,655	15,000	0	5,000
Optical disk storage drive	32,100	0	32,100	15,000	17,100	15,000	0	15,000
Office renovation	50,000	0	50,000	18,500	31,500	0	0	18,500
Dictation system	195,040	0	195,040	155,000	40,040	0	0	155,000
Office renovation	0	(5,000)	(5,000)	3,000	(8,000)	0	0	3,000
Dictation system	0	5,000	5,000	2,000	3,000	0	0	2,000
Hospital 1	0	0	0	0	0	687,037	0	0
Total	**$2,108,658**	**$(5,000)**	**$2,103,658**	**$519,575**	**$1,584,083**	**$828,587**	**$241,609**	**$277,966**

Source: Kaufman, Hall & Associates, Inc. Used with permission.

plan. How can the project be improved? Should it be halted or delayed? Assumptions about related or similar projects may need to be revised.

Organizational leaders must have and foster an understanding that not all projects for which capital is allocated will be successful. Because this is an axiom of business planning, it is vital that each capital request includes specific metrics that define the point at which the plug is pulled on underperforming investments and the specific exit strategy that will be implemented in such an instance.

Many healthcare organizations wait far too long to either modify or terminate a bad capital investment decision (McCanna 2005). The occurrence and sophistication of post-allocation project review and validation of projected returns from capital investments, in fact, vary considerably by organization. A survey that included some of the nation's most sophisticated health systems indicated that many systems are only in the early stages of developing and implementing processes to monitor returns and expected investment performance (Sussman 2005). Some systems perform feasibility updates or retrospective reviews approximately one year after a project has been up and running, regardless of when it was approved. Chief financial officers at the hospital units typically perform the post-allocation analyses, which are reviewed at system level by corporate finance staff. Consistency, standardization, and comprehensiveness of the review process are often lacking. This results in diminution of the process's ability to enhance and inform decision making in these organizations.

To give the post-approval process "teeth," the council should consider the following strategies:

- Require review of all approved projects for at least three years postallocation, which would include at least the first full year of the projects' operations
- Require retrospective review of all approved projects as a prerequisite to submission of capital requests in subsequent year's capital management processes
- Share the retrospective review directly with the organization's board
- Create a direct link between capital approval and the operating budget (Allocation of capital predicated on achieving operating efficiencies should result in direct and specific reductions in departmental operating budgets)

Disciplined use of a best-practice post-allocation process supports the rigor of the overall capital management process. A multiyear strategy for implementing a best-practice process and ongoing education and communication regarding that process—the topics of the final chapter—ensure the thorough integration of the capital management process with the organization's ongoing planning and decision-making processes.

References

Grube, M. E., and T. L. Wareham. 2005. "What is Your Game Plan? Advice from the Capital Markets." *Healthcare Financial Management* 59 (11): 63–75.

McCanna, P. J. 2005. "In Essentials of Integrated Strategic Financial Planning and Capital Allocation." Financing the Future II Series. Westchester, IL: Healthcare Financial Management Association.

Sussman, J. H. 2005. *Survey of Capital Allocation Approaches in 26 U.S. Health Systems*. Skokie, IL: Kaufman, Hall & Associates, Inc.

CHAPTER 9

Making It Happen

THE SUCCESSFUL ROLLOUT of a high-quality capital management process requires commitment to that process throughout the organization. The commitment must originate from the top leaders, and it must pervade all levels of management. Education, communication, and a solid implementation plan with a realistic time frame, as described here, help to secure such commitment.

The Role of Education

All too often, the capital allocation and management process is viewed strictly as a finance function. However, experience shows that including nonfinancial managers is critical to effective, best-practice capital management. Key organizational constituents must have a strong knowledge base about the principles of corporate finance and understand the capital management process and its time frame. The entire management team should have at least a basic understanding of the corporate finance concepts embodied in effective decision making.

Much can be learned from such corporate finance leaders as GE, which pioneered the organization-wide application of a rigorous capital management process. At GE, everybody—from secretaries to senior vice presidents—knows the requirements and timing of the planning and allocation processes, including when proposals for capital projects must be submitted and when the decision making will occur. They also know how capital requests will be evaluated—the criteria that will be used—and what requests have been approved and those that were not approved.

Extensive ongoing education and communication are required to achieve this exceptional level of transparency. Such courses as "Finance for Nonfinance People" and "Finance 101 for Operating Managers" are offered organization-wide at GE to achieve staff buy-in to the need for and importance of rigorous financial and capital planning and capital management processes (see Sidebar 9-1).

Quantitative analytical tools used in corporate finance may be new to some, particularly department manager–level staff, and may require in-depth education and training, both initially and on an ongoing basis. Increased knowledge about tools and techniques directed beyond the finance department and into line-management positions is the most effective means to ensure institutionalization of the best-practice capital management process.

The finance staff cannot and should not be expected to perform all of the analytical work associated with submissions of capital requests. Neither should the finance staff be the only organizational staff familiar with the required analytics. Requests for capital are often generated from the grass roots of a healthcare organization; such requests frequently represent clinical initiatives to support improved patient care quality or service volume growth. The inclusion of clinical staff in the capital management education process empowers clinicians and technical staff to generate valid ideas, to perform the related quantitative and qualitative analysis, and to effectively present their projects within the structure of the capital management process. This creates two major benefits at an organizational level: (1) minimizing potential end runs around the process, and (2) enhancing overall financial IQ.

Because a sound capital management process relies on quantitative techniques, such as NPV analysis, it is vital that implementation of the process be carried out by people with a working knowledge of the proper use of NPV, including its theory and application. Technical training must be available to anyone within the organization who will be submitting proposed capital projects for review. The training must be geared to educate staff members who come from a broad range of educational and occupational backgrounds, from formally trained financial analysts to self-taught departmental administrators. The goal is to provide all staff with a common language and approach to project analysis and to ensure that the staff maintains

---

Sidebar 9-1. Finance 101 for Operating Managers

Following is the overview text of GE's basic finance course for operating managers:

Business performance is generally measured in financial terms by ROI. The higher the profits relative to the investment in assets, the better it appears that the firm is doing. ROI, however, is only one measure of how well a company is doing. Other measures relate to a firm's ability to manage cash and assets.

In this module, you will learn how a business obtains and invests its cash to generate profits. By managing profitability, liquidity, solvency, and efficiency, operating managers play an important role in determining the success of the firm. The module's objectives are to:

- Understand the basic goals of any business entity
- Understand the basic goals of financial management
- Learn the dynamics of the cash cycle of the firm, its four phases, and the key management issues that each phase addresses

Key topics include: goals of the firm; goals of financial management (profitability, liquidity, solvency, efficiency); and cash cycle of the firm.

Source: GE Commercial Finance. Used with permission.

---

enough of a comfort level to encourage continued, active participation in the process.

Education that successfully supports the capital management process has two key characteristics. First, the education is ongoing. Learning about methods and concepts that may be somewhat foreign, especially when that new skill set will be applied only on an episodic basis, is like trying to learn a foreign language in one class. Participants deserve and will often demand ongoing educational opportunities aimed at enhancing their ability to analyze and present strategic capital opportunities in a manner that improves the chances of that investment being approved. In some organizations, this means quarterly, semiannual, or annual sessions to review basic concepts and delve further into more advanced techniques.

The second characteristic of successful education is its use of a curriculum that provides a broader understanding of how to evaluate the strategic financial impact of potential projects. The curriculum must cover various methods of analyzing different types of projects. For example, how should the cost of *not* replacing assets be factored into the evaluation of an investment proposal? Is there a best-practice approach to assessing potential cannibalization effects of a proposed project? Finally, what is the appropriate use of sensitivity analysis in the assessment of a proposed investment?

Many organizations fail to consistently provide the resources needed for appropriate and effective education. However, given the importance and long-term impact of the decisions associated with capital management, the cost of not having such a process is incalculable.

In designing an ongoing education program, executives should consider the following questions:

- How does the organization ensure that staff members have access to the right tools to perform the required analysis?
- How does the organization provide staff with the necessary education to evaluate complex projects?
- How often should that education be provided?
- How can the organization ensure consistent application of project definitions and quantitative techniques?
- What benchmarks can the organization provide to give decision makers guidance to screen bad projects?

During the early years of best-practice process implementation, the capabilities of project sponsors and the resulting quality of their analytical assumptions and presentations may be highly inconsistent. A continuing, broad education effort is needed to minimize such variation, which can create disparities in the ability to acquire capital.

The Role of Communication

Comprehensive communication of all aspects of the process—including steps in the actual allocation and management process, process methodologies, basic principles of corporate finance, project-based analysis, and the process calendar—is essential to success. The potential impact of the capital management process on the organization's decision-making processes demands extensive communication among all those involved in the process, especially in the first few years of implementation. Communication routes must be broad, deep, and multidirectional, including the board of directors, senior management, department directors, and clinicians.

Although the specific communication strategy will differ by organization, there are three basic modes of communication required for successful process implementation:

1. *Up-front communication.* This communication should provide a full description of the planned capital management process, including its objectives, timing, informational requirements, and approval structure. All associated decision support tools should be provided with detailed instructions for their use.
2. *Ongoing communication.* As the capital management process unfolds, a continuous stream of communication should be maintained through all levels of the organization. This will ensure proper usage of all support tools, avoidance of delays in project analysis, consistency of technical approach, and correction of process or technical errors in an expeditious manner.
3. *Feedback.* As difficulties in the process are identified, the organization should have a structured means of learning of such issues and providing updated, corrected information to the field. These communications should be funneled through a singular source to ensure consistent dissemination of information throughout the organization.

Implementing the capital management process requires careful planning and execution of an ongoing communication plan. It is impossible to communicate too much about how analyses will be evaluated, by whom, and what the criteria will be. Armed with full information, members of the organization can make correct, informed decisions that further the organization's objectives.

Effective supporting materials are vital as an ongoing reference. Written materials describing the process and how to participate offer an effective implementation tool and can also provide basic information on corporate finance principles. The target of such materials should be middle management and senior management and can be as basic as needed to encourage participation in the process. At one organization, an education presentation was developed and recorded so that each new employee can view the video as part of his or her orientation. That organization is not only educating the new employee but also establishing the organizational importance of the capital management process.

Decentralizing the capital management process through education and communication will also increase its efficiency and effectiveness. To accomplish broad decentralization, champions can be used to support implementation and provide an ongoing resource. Sidebar 9-2 describes typical barriers to the successful rollout of a best-practice capital management process and strategies to overcome such barriers.

Implementation Plan and Time Frame

Complete implementation of a smoothly running best-practice capital management process is likely to be a two-year or three-year process. During the first year, the interim objective should be for managers to buy into the process as a step in the right direction. This involves adoption of the analytical tools and adherence to the process schedule. The first-year goal is fundamentally to raise the financial IQ of the organization and establish the process.

During the second year, as managers continue to learn to live within the process, the objective is to ensure application of the concepts and approaches to all areas of decision making.

By year three, the best-practice capital management process should have evolved to be an integral part of what managers do. At this stage, managers will be able to automatically screen bad projects from the process and understand the critical link between strategic planning and financial planning.

To evaluate implementation progress, leaders should ask the following questions:

• Has the number of projects coming in through the back door been reduced or eliminated?

Sidebar 9-2. Barriers to the Successful Implementation of a Best-Practice Capital Management Process and Strategies to Overcome Such Barriers

Avoidance

Expressed as "The process involves too much work," this barrier is a function of lack of awareness of the magnitude of the decisions being made and the implications of inappropriate decisions. Overcoming this objection is accomplished through transparency—by providing information about the variety and significance of the investments being evaluated. If the projects are not worth the up-front analysis, why would they be worth the investment?

Misperception

Expressed as "My project is different and shouldn't have to go through the usual capital management process," this barrier is exacerbated in an environment where decision making does not employ a corporate finance, analytically based approach. Use of the common language of NPV, described in Chapter Six, and other corporate finance tools can overcome this problem. The objective quantification of financial return and the application of portfolio-based decision making will ensure that each project is evaluated on an equal footing.

Misunderstanding

Expressed as "This is a defensive project—its benefits cannot be quantified," this barrier reflects the classic, political capital decision-making process. By claiming the project's unique ability to defend the organization, the project champion moves the decision from an analytical framework to a political and emotional one. This is especially true for projects with little or no potential return. To overcome this barrier, emphasis must be focused on quantifying those aspects of the project that can be quantified and on the cost of not investing in the project.

Subversion

Expressed as "I will just go to the CEO; the CEO always approves what I want," this barrier can be overcome very simply by the CEO's explicit endorsement and adoption of the formal capital management process. This forces decisions out of the hallway or private office and into a public conference room.

Source: Kaufman, Hall & Associates, Inc. Used with permission.

- Are the requirements for project analytics effectively decreasing the number of politically based projects?
- Has the quality of project analysis improved since standardized project-review requirements were established?
- Has the general caliber of the submitted projects improved?
- Are the projects more consistent with organizational strategy and more focused on market growth and overall return?

If the answer to any or all of these questions is "yes," the organization has made significant progress toward successful implementation of corporate finance–based capital management.

As described throughout this book, the ultimate goal of a best-practice capital management process is to deploy the organization's capital in a way that is most likely to support its overall strategy and generate additional capital capacity for future investment. Performance at a survival-only level may not actually ensure future survival, and it certainly does not achieve competitive performance. Every small step taken toward that ultimate goal helps the organization improve its competitive financial position and enables it to pursue aggressive and effective strategies.

The capital management process must be designed to evolve and change over time. The process should be reviewed annually to assess progress toward meeting specified goals. This will involve looking at what works and why, what does not work and why, what needs to be added, and what components are unnecessary and can be eliminated.

Ongoing review of the process, in fact, should be a formal component of the process structure and should occur at approximately the same time each year. Organizations must be willing and able to adjust the process to meet its evolving internal and external needs. For example, adjustments may need to be made to the schedule, analytical components, and definitions of threshold and non-threshold capital. Individuals participating in the process at both the leadership and department levels should be empowered to suggest necessary changes to enhance the process.

After all is said and done, the most critical factor for success is patience. It is likely to take two or three years before the capital management process runs as it was designed. Ingrained organizational behavior cannot be altered quickly. This is especially true of behavior that is integral to the operational and political machinations of the organization. In many organizations, capital-related decisions are highly politicized, often used as a means to give benefits to key constituencies within the organization. Implementation of a corporate finance–based capital management process in such organizations will likely represent a significant change. Making that change and achieving the results will take time.

Implementation Example: Capital Allocation in Practice

This example describes one organization's recent implementation of a corporate finance–based capital management process. Although the name of the organization is fictitious, the information provided is real.

The Organization at a Glance

Regional Health System (RHS) is the largest healthcare network in the state. A fully integrated system covering the north and central regions of the state, it owns and operates 11 acute care hospitals. The system has 2,000 licensed beds and a staff of nearly 9,600 employees. The system's nonacute care operations include skilled nursing facilities, senior housing facilities, home care agencies, occupational health services, hospices, primary care clinics, fitness facilities, and a 150,000-member preferred provider organization. In its most recent fiscal year, RHS generated approximately $1.7 billion in gross revenue and was rated "A2" by Moody's Investors Service.

Previous Capital Management Process

The capital management process in place at RHS during the late 1990s and early 2000s resembled the process used by many healthcare organizations. The amount of capital available to support the organization's development during a specified time period—the capital constraint—was devised by looking at the annual cash budget rather than by considering the organization's total capital capacity and long-range financial plan.

Financial planning had a firm place in RHS's culture (the good news), but it was not as rigorous as that offered by a corporate finance–based approach (the bad news). The process used to evaluate and approve proposed capital investments was as follows.

Each facility or entity in the system prepared a three-year to five-year plan, outlining major projects and capital needs. The corporate finance team used these lists to prepare a matrix of the wish lists by facility/entity, by item, and by year. The management executive committee reviewed the wish-list matrix and, having calculated a capital constraint and being aware of the dollars available to be spent, determined how much and where capital dollars would be spent.

In the previous capital management process at RHS, capital requests were separated into routine items and strategic items. Routine items, typically requiring a lower dollar allocation, received capital based on historical spending patterns. Strategic items were defined as "all projects in excess of $500,000." These were often lump sums of unidentified, loosely defined individual projects (for example, "new facilities for $2 million"). Routine capital requests received funding first, which limited the dollars available for allocation to strategic capital requirements.

Financial analysis of projects was limited. Detailed analyses generally were not prepared until immediately before beginning a project or spending the funds and thus were not critical to the up-front project evaluation. Projects were approved in a serial fashion, which meant that project funding could disappear if the organization's financial performance changed before a project started drawing on funds.

Without the consistent and simultaneous comparative evaluation of multiple projects, it was very difficult for RHS to optimize its portfolio of capital investment opportunities. In addition, without a formal process for making capital allocation decisions, the management executive committee often made decisions based solely on subjective and, at times, unstated criteria.

The Impetus for a New Process

A number of factors provided the impetus for a new approach to allocating capital. Like many healthcare organizations, RHS management was concerned about lack of net revenue growth. Managed care reimbursement constraints and the effects of federal regulatory changes had created considerable pressure on RHS's net revenue. Quite simply, fewer dollars were coming into the system. Yet capital requests of all kinds continued at a high level and were growing, creating a disparity between the dollars available to meet capital needs and those requested. Because operations were not able to generate additional return, the system relied increasingly on investment returns from cash reserves and selected capital projects to maintain profitability and liquidity targets.

When income from operations and investment returns began to slide, RHS leaders started to express concern about the serial approach to project approval. They recognized that the projects on the radar screen first, in fact, may not be those of the highest strategic priority or with the highest potential return for the organization. Had they evaluated the whole group of projects on the front end, the leaders acknowledged that the mix of projects receiving funding might have been quite different. With these concerns identified and becoming increasingly acute, RHS leaders embraced the need to create a rigorous capital management process based on corporate finance principles.

Redesign Objectives

The central objectives for the redesign of RHS's capital management process were as follows:

- Objective decision making
- A fixed, predetermined process
- Enhanced and decentralized analysis
- Comparative review of projects
- Quantification of decision making.

To address these objectives, RHS established a task force of key members of financial and operating management from both the corporate office and from operating entities throughout the system. This approach helped to ensure organization-wide participation in process design, sensitivity to operating and management issues generated by various design options, and ownership of the new process. Task force members included the executive vice president of hospital operations, the senior vice president of regional hospital operations, the system's CFO, two major hospital CEOs (one from an urban hospital and one from a regional hospital), the senior vice president of ambulatory services, the medical director, and three members of the corporate finance staff.

Process Redesign

The task force concentrated its capital management process redesign efforts on five distinct areas. The first was to define the principles and objectives of a systemwide approach to capital management. The group identified the need to disconnect current allocation of capital from past spending patterns. The historical benchmark approach did not allow the organization to respond adequately to changing market and financial conditions. Further, a status quo approach impeded consideration of potentially promising new investment opportunities.

The task force also focused on the need for equal access to system-generated dollars for capital projects; moving away from "you eat what you kill" mentality. Each entity in the system would have access to the system's total available dollars through a well-defined and well-articulated capital management process for the system as a whole.

Second, the task force redefined how to calculate the capital constraint, agreeing that a specific calculation would cover all capital requirements, not simply available cash. The team's capital constraint calculation appears as Table 9-1. Note that the "Uses of cash" portion in the figure includes a systemwide 10 percent capital contingency pool for emergencies.

The task force also segregated cash uses into those below (nonthreshold capital) or above (threshold capital) a minimum dollar threshold. For ease of initial implementation, RHS retained $500,000 as its evaluation threshold and agreed to reevaluate that dollar sum on an annual basis. A complete financial analysis was required for all projects with a cost of $500,000 or greater.

The task force allocated approximately $14 million of the cash available for capital to fund nonthreshold capital requests and a significantly larger $23

TABLE 9-1. The Capital Constraint Calculation at RHS

	Strategic Financial Plan ($000s)
Sources of cash	
Operating income	$17,249
Add: Depreciation and amortization	49,381
Other income sources (uses)	(2,975)
Use of funded depreciation	10,000
Total sources of cash	73,655
Uses of cash	
Retirement of long-term debt	(11,737)
Increase in working capital	(18,554)
Carryover from prior-year approvals of capital	(3,130)
Total uses of cash (excluding capital)	(33,421)
Total cash available for capital	40,234
Less 10% emergency capital contingency	(4,023)
Net cash available for allocation	36,211
Less cash allocated to nonthreshold capital	(13,608)
Cash available for threshold capital	$22,602

Source: Reprinted from Kaufman, K. 2006. *Best-Practice Financial Management: Six Key Concepts for Healthcare Leaders*, 3rd ed. Chicago: Health Administration Press. Used with permission.

million to threshold capital requests. This split was expected to help ensure that strategic investment was provided a sufficient piece of the total capital pie.

The third task tackled by the task force was to create a means to allocate dollars for nonthreshold capital to system entities in a way that would reward performance. This would remove a significant part of the subjectivity of a political approach to allocating capital and provide financial support to meet minimum needs. Departmentally generated capital requests would continue to be managed locally, but the dollars available to the entity for such capital would now be allocated based on the long-term profitability of the requesting entity as measured by its relative EBITDA contribution to the system. Nonprofitable, nonrevenue-generating, and small entities would receive a minimum allocation of the available nonthreshold pool to fund vital needs. All entities were provided data on the design of nonthreshold capital allocation so that gaming would be minimized or eliminated. Table 9-2 provides a look at allocation of nonthreshold capital.

The task force's fourth area of focus was to establish consistent analytical standards for all threshold capital projects. The task force communicated the analytic requirements systemwide and encouraged decentralized analysis. Regional Health System's investment in state-of-the-art financial decision software and educational efforts supporting the software and its tools made decentralized analysis possible, and indeed, was expected within each entity.

The task force's fifth and final task was to create a practical capital management schedule. To this end, the task force defined a process calendar that was consistent with and integrated with the organization's ongoing planning and implementation processes. Leaders of RHS committed to a calendar-driven approach to planning and implementation, codified that approach, and communicated specific timing requirements systemwide. During the first year of implementation, the calendar was modified somewhat to provide extra time for proper project analysis.

Regional Health System chartered a capital management council as the system's decision-making body. The council included RHS's CEO, COO, CFO, senior vice president of operations, and a physician vice president of one of the facilities. "The goal was to avoid a large-group capital management decision-making process that would involve various constituencies with different agendas and different axes to grind," described RHS's vice president of finance, who served the council in a support role.

Meeting Implementation Challenges and Evaluating the New Process

Regional Health System's implementation of a redesigned capital allocation process was a multiyear process that required continuous monitoring, evaluation, and evolution to ensure the best possible results.

Table 9-2. Allocation of Nonthreshold Capital

Department	Adjusted EBITDA	Allocable EBITDA	% of Total EBITDA	Allocation of $13,608	Allocation Adjustments to Minimum ($)	Allocation of $13,608	Final Allocation Percentage
Hospital A	$38,373	$ 38,373	38.3 %	$ 5,206	—	$ 4,394	32.3 %
Hospital B	29,839	29,839	29.8	4,049	—	3,417	25.1
Hospital C	13,530	13,530	13.5	1,836	—	1,549	11.4
Hospital D	5,060	5,060	5.0	687	—	579	4.3
Hospital E	340	340	0.3	46	$125	125	0.9
Hospital F	905	905	0.9	123	125	125	0.9
Hospital G	3,118	3,118	3.1	423	750	750	5.5
Hospital H	845	845	0.8	115	370	370	2.7
Hospital I	—	—	0.0	—	—	—	0.0
Hospital J	8,286	8,286	8.3	1,124	—	949	7.0
Hospital K	—	—	0.0	—	—	—	0.0
Central business office	—	—	0.0	—	100	100	0.7
Laundry	—	—	0.0	—	100	100	0.7
Information systems	—	—	0.0	—	750	750	5.5
Corporate services	(45,549)	—	0.0	—	400	400	2.9
Education	—	—	0.0	—	—	—	0.0
Health centers	—	—	0.0	—	—	—	0.0
Total RHS	**$54,747**	**$100,296**	**100.0 %**	**$13,608**	**$2,720**	**$13,608**	**100.0 %**

Source: Reprinted from Kaufman, K. 2006. *Best-Practice Financial Management: Six Key Concepts for Healthcare Leaders*, 3rd ed. Chicago: Health Administration Press. Used with permission.

Year One

During its first year, RHS's new corporate finance–based capital management process achieved two major accomplishments: (1) improved analysis and (2) enhanced support of the decision-making process. Project champions in entities throughout the system were able to prepare appropriate and improved analyses. "To devise realistic reimbursement assumptions, for example, the reimbursement staff needed to understand a proposed project and carefully think through how the project would be reimbursed. Global assumptions may not have been applicable," noted the system's vice president of finance. Decentralized analyses ensured accurate and detailed financial input.

Training time related to the analytics was required during the first year for both corporate and facility-based staff. Everyone needed to understand that politics was being removed from the capital management process. To some extent, it took failure to get a project approved in year one for staff to understand the magnitude of the change.

With individual and comparative project data at its fingertips, the council was able to make better-informed decisions. Through the decision support structure provided within the newly implemented financial software, the council defined the qualitative and quantitative criteria to be used to select a portfolio of capital investments. The review criteria were weighted: two-thirds weight was assigned to financial criteria, and one-third was related to other criteria such as community service and physician issues. "This weighting made approval of an unprofitable project an explicit event, visible to everyone in the system," said the vice president of finance.

As it continually revised the structure of the selected portfolio, the software enabled the council to see the quantitative impact of its decisions on a real-time basis. Use of a best-practice capital management process enabled RHS to look at the whole picture. If the analytics for a certain project showed that the project would not meet financial criteria, but the capital management council felt the project needed to be approved for community service reasons, the council now knew what the financial shortfall would be and could address how to balance or make up for that shortfall. Everyone became aware of the financial consequences of the decisions they were making.

Fewer projects made it to the table for discussion. Instead of extensive wish lists, only projects that were able to pass the rigor of the local review process were submitted for consideration. "In the first year alone, perhaps 15 projects never made it to the council, because the staff didn't want to go through the analytics or thought that the project could not survive the analysis," said the vice president of finance. A project evaluation form, an important tool included in the state-of-the-art software, added discipline to the analyses. Because everyone used the same method of presenting and evaluating a project, a direct apples-to-apples comparison was possible.

The efficiency of the new process encouraged members of the council and system managers alike. In an all-day meeting scheduled for review of 58 projects, the council not only covered its agenda but also finished earlier than expected. The review process was not an agonizing, exhausting one because the information needed for decision making was in front of everyone. Managers throughout the system thought the process was fair, and even if an entity's project was not approved, its champions understood why. After the first year of implementation, RHS leaders were satisfied that corporate finance–based capital management represented a step in the right direction.

Year Two

During the second year of implementation, RHS focused on fine-tuning the new capital management process, concentrating on such areas as the criteria used to allocate capital to the corporate office and the structure of access to contingency funds. The RHS corporate office includes capital-intensive areas, such as financial operations, information technology, centralized billing, and a laundry. Because these operations do not produce cash flow, the task force needed to find a means other than EBITDA to make appropriate amounts of capital available to them.

During the first year of the new process, RHS wrestled with how to handle capital allocated to the corporate office. "In year one, we set a lower level of $25,000 for corporate's threshold capital. This was a mistake because so many more projects now needed to be reviewed," said the vice president of finance.

During year two, RHS reconfigured the nonthreshold allocation by fixing a minimum allocation to the corporate office and each component operation and applying the consistent $500,000 threshold to all projects, including those generated by the corporate office. In effect, services such as IT and the corporate billing office became their own entities subject to the same threshold capital requirements of all other facilities.

In the area of emergency capital contingency, RHS increased the size of the contingency to ensure control of total capital spending and emphasized substitution of capital projects as a first means to meet emergency or off-cycle needs. The council strictly controlled access to contingency funds.

Year two's benefits included the following:

- Even better project analysis by champions and champion teams
- Continued self-imposed weeding out of marginal projects by the individual entities before reaching the council
- Reduced corporate project review requirements
- Increased focus by senior management to maintain the integrity of the process

After the second year of implementation, RHS leaders were satisfied that they had fully applied the fundamentals of the corporate finance–based capital management process and had learned how to apply it to nongrowth areas, such as corporate office functions. "We now knew how many dollars we could spend and could make capital allocation decisions based on solid financial criteria. The quantitative analysis provided a real comfort level about the bottom line results we could achieve," said the vice president of finance.

Areas for Continued Vigilance and Future Efforts

By year three, corporate finance–based capital management had become "just a part of what we do" at RHS. However, continued vigilance will be required in the future. Leaders will need to stick to the decisions made during the management process. To facilitate this, RHS has implemented a process that monitors month-to-month project progress and that informs council members and operating-entity managers how each of their decisions is affecting RHS's long-term financial success.

Leaders at RHS also recognize the need to follow through to monitor the projects selected for funding. Actual project progress is being tracked against project analyses submitted at the approval stage. Data related to project-specific performance is being captured and analyzed. Project updates are required as a precursor to an entity submitting capital requests in subsequent years. The financial impact of decisions made and potential changes to those decisions are being quantified on an ongoing basis. "Information related to assumptions that did or did not turn out to be true needs to be available and reviewed before the next capital allocation process begins," said the vice president of finance.

Future efforts at RHS will focus on the following:

- Continuing education to broaden and deepen analytical capabilities systemwide
- Increased sophistication of project monitoring
- Use of portfolio management techniques to ensure the best possible mix of capital projects
- Extending the process to the individual unit level for application to nonthreshold capital projects

In year three of the new capital management process, RHS leaders are firmly committed to the belief that guessing just does not work anymore. A rigorous, corporate finance–based capital management process is the only way to effectively integrate long-term strategies and current-year capital investment.

Closing Comments

Effective capital management is organized around the concepts described in this book—namely, articulated objectives and principles; defined, standardized methodologies; clear governance and accountability; a known calendar; effective implementation; and ongoing education and communication.

Implementation of a rigorous, corporate finance–based capital management process represents a significant organizational change for most healthcare organizations. Because of the resistance of managers or executives who are accustomed to making independent capital decisions and the frustrations that often accompany the iterative nature of the new process, implementation of a best-practice capital management process may not be popular initially.

The benefits of a best-practice process, however, are well worth the effort of meeting the challenges during the transition period. The discipline, rigor, and analytic standards of a best-practice capital management process bring to all constituents recognition of the importance of proactively managing capital spending. The collaborative and transparent nature of the process provides a strategic focus for the whole organization and ensures organization-wide consistency in how dollars are spent.

A best-practice process fully integrates strategic planning with financial and capital planning. Capital can be approved based on the initiatives' consistency with strategic goals within agreed-upon financial and risk parameters; capital can be denied based on concrete strategic and financial reasons rather than on political positioning.

An improved process not only identifies projects most likely to bring strategic financial success, but it also keeps bad ideas off the table. This results in fewer disasters for the organization in the longer term and an improved bottom line.

Will organizations continue to have good capital management processes when they have good bottom lines, or will they lose the discipline? Will profitability be sustainable? In almost all healthcare organizations, capital appetites routinely exceed capital constraints. This fact will create continued need for a disciplined best-practice capital management process. Choices will always need to be made. Political influence will always need to be countered by the discipline provided by corporate finance–based decision making.

Circling back to this book's opening words, in an environment of scarce resources, increasing competition, and significant requirements for capital investment, healthcare executives nationwide must allocate available capital to those initiatives that will best meet the strategic objectives of their organizations while enhancing financial performance. The best-practice capital management process described in this book offers executives an effective approach to making the decisions that will ensure their organizations' strategic and financial competitive performance in the future. Implement the approach. Advance the discipline.

About the Author

JASON H. SUSSMAN is a partner of Kaufman, Hall & Associates, Inc. His experience includes all aspects of financial planning and financial advisory services for hospitals, healthcare systems, and physician groups. His areas of expertise include strategic financial planning, capital allocation and management, mergers and acquisitions, and various financing transactions.

Prior to joining Kaufman, Hall & Associates, Inc., in 1990, Mr. Sussman directed the Chicago Capital Finance Group of a national accounting firm's healthcare consulting practice. His consulting there related to assessment of financial feasibility, mergers and acquisitions, business plan development, and capital plan development. Prior to this, Mr. Sussman was the special assistant to the president at Michael Reese Hospital and Medical Center in Chicago, responsible for the certificate-of-need and capital-budgeting processes at the institution.

Mr. Sussman has authored articles for various industry periodicals, including *Healthcare Financial Management*, and was a contributing author to all three editions of *Best-Practice Financial Management: Six Key Concepts for Healthcare Leaders*, *The Financially Competitive Healthcare Organization*, and *Topics in Health Care Finance*. He has presented programs at seminars sponsored by the American College of Healthcare Executives (ACHE), American Hospital Association, Healthcare Financial Management Association (HFMA), National Association of

Children's Hospitals and Related Institutions, and various state hospital associations.

Mr. Sussman holds a master of business administration in finance and accounting, with a specialization in healthcare management, from Northwestern University's Kellogg Graduate School of Management in Evanston, Illinois, and a bachelor of arts from the Johns Hopkins University in Baltimore, Maryland. He has a CPA certificate in Illinois and is a member of HFMA and ACHE.